Common Building Defects

Diagnosis and Remedy

compiled by

The National Building Agency

*and originally issued as Part 2 of the
NBA's Housing Association Maintenance
Training Course*

This volume is published by Longman Group UK
Limited by arrangement with the National Building
Agency. It first appeared as Part II of the NBA's
Housing Association Maintenance Training Scheme.

Longman Scientific & Technical
Longman Group UK Limited
Longman House, Burnt Mill, Harlow,
Essex CM20 2JE, England
and Associated Companies throughout the world

First published 1979
Reprinted 1982, 1984, 1985
Reprinted by Longman Scientific & Technical 1987, 1989, 1990

ISBN 0-582-41393-1

Produced by Longman Group (FE) Limited
Printed in Hong Kong

Acknowledgements

NBA wishes to acknowledge the advice and assistance of members of the Steering Group nominated by the Housing Corporation and the National Federation of Housing Associations, who sponsored this work:

Julian Ashby	Circle 33 Housing Trust
Rosemary Bloxam	Notting Hill Housing Trust
Andrew Fellowes and Dorcas Ward	Family Housing Association
Jeff Spoors	North Housing Group
Tony Stanford	National Federation of Housing Associations
Clive Watkins	Housing Corporation.

In preparing this book, extensive use has been made of information in 'Common defects in buildings' by H J Eldridge, published in 1976 by Her Majesty's Stationery Office to whom grateful acknowledgement is made. That book covers the subject comprehensively and forms an excellent reference base for professional and technical staff involved in building maintenance. However this book is aimed at a less technical audience, and deals with many problems by suggesting that the non-technical reader should refer all but the simplest problems to a surveyor. Nevertheless simple explanations of the more technical defects are included since these may well be of interest to anyone actively concerned with housing management and will help to ensure that clear and useful information is passed on to the professional concerned.

Contents

INTRODUCTION

Diagnosis of defects 10
Causes of defects 11
How to use this book 14
How to use the defect sheets 14
Example of use of this book 16

DEFECT SHEETS

EXTERNAL WALLS AND CHIMNEYS A 18
Cracked brickwork A1 20
Cracking, splitting and bending of
    chimney stacks A2 22
Crumbling of brickwork mortar joints A3 24
Crumbling of bricks A4 26
Movement of brickwork including
    squeezing out of damp-proof course A5 28
Flaking of rendering on brickwork A6 30
Horizontal cracking of rendering on
    brickwork A7 32
Random cracking of rendering on
    brickwork A8 34
Blistering of paintwork to rendering
    and cladding A9 36

ROOFS, GUTTERS AND RAINWATER
    PIPES B 38
Blistering, splitting and cracking of
    asphalt roof surfaces B1 40
Blistering, splitting and rippling of
    bitumen felt roof surfaces B2 42
Sagging and deformation B3 44
Deteriorating and slipping roof tiles B4 46
Deteriorating and slipping roof slates B5 48
Leaking gutters B6 50
Blocked or leaking rainwater pipes B7 52

WINDOWS, DOORS AND EXTERNAL
    JOINERY C 54
Timber decay C1 56

Contents

Deterioration of paintwork and putty	C2	58
Distortion of timber windows	C3	60
Cracking of glass in steel windows	C4	62
External delamination of plywood panels	C5	64
Distortion of timber doors	C6	66
FINISHES TO INTERNAL WALLS, CEIL- INGS AND JOINERY; INTERNAL DOORS	D	68
Cracks related to movement in the buil- ding structure	D1	70
Shrinkage cracks	D2	72
Cracks associated with differential movement	D3	74
Full thickness of plaster loose	D4	76
Top coat of plaster loose	D5	78
Pitting of plasterwork	D6	80
Discoloured and blistered decoration	D7	82
Tiles loose or falling off	D8	84
Peeling finishes on joinery	D9	86
Faulty door operation	D10	88
Peeling and flaking paintwork	D11	90
FLOORS	E	92
Collapsed suspended timber floor	E1	94
Warping and shrinking floorboards	E2	96
Lifting, curling and cracking of concrete screeds	E3	98
Lifting and cracking of concrete floors	E4	100
Sweating and disintegration of magnesite (composition) floor surfaces	E5	102
Lifting of wood blocks	E6	104
Lifting of clay tiles	E7	106
Lifting and deterioration of plastic floor tiles	E8	108
Loss of adhesion of sheet flooring	E9	110
PLUMBING, HEATING AND DRAINS	F	112
Leaks in galvanised cold water tanks	F1	114
Leaks at joints	F2	116
Frozen pipes	F3	118
Furring of pipes	F4	120
Malfunctioning ball valves	F5	122

Contents

Water hammer/knocking pipes   F6   124

Softening and distortion of plastic waste
    pipes and traps   F7   126

Blocked waste pipes   F8   128

Blocked drains   F9   130

Boiler or water heater not working
    properly   F10   132

Radiators not working properly   F11   134

Warm air heating not working properly   F12   136

ELECTRICITY SUPPLY AND
    DISTRIBUTION   G   138

Failure of electrical insulation   G1   140

Electrical appliance not working   G2   142

DAMP   H   144

Damp in basements   H1   146

Semi-permanent damp   H2   148

Damp solid wall associated with rain   H3   150

Damp cavity wall associated with rain   H4   152

Patchy damp not associated with rain   H5   154

General damp not associated with rain   H6   156

Damp chimney breast   H7   158

Damp wall or ceiling   H8   160

Damp ceiling under flat roof   H9   162

Damp ceiling under pitched roof   H10   164

Persistent damp   H11   166

Damp not associated with rain or
    condensation   H12   168

DEFECTS IN APPEARANCE   J   170

Dirty patches   J1   172

Patchy white deposits   J2   174

Algae, lichen and mosses   J3   176

Mould growth   J4   178

MATERIALS   K   180

Dry rot   K1   182

Wet rot   K2   184

Woodworm   K3   186

Corrosion   K4   188

Shrunk or sagging sealants   K5   190

Contents.

BIBLIOGRAPHY   192

INDEX   193

Preface

Building maintenance is an expensive item requiring careful attention from building owners, occupiers, contractors, surveyors, architects and in fact every active member of the construction industry. The correct diagnosis of building defects associated with the correct remedial action is the only economic basis for a successful building maintenance programme. This practical volume is designed to help diagnosis and give an indication of the remedy for the situation discovered.

This book was originally prepared by the National Building Agency (NBA) as Part II of its Maintenance Training Package for housing assistants on the staff of housing associations, but such is its scope and value that many people will find its contents of day-to-day practical relevance. Useful cross references are made in this book to Parts I and III of this Maintenance Training Package but this work stands as a valuable work of reference in its own right.

DIAGNOSIS OF DEFECTS

Defect diagnosis is simply a logical way of proceeding
from the evidence to the cause of a defect, after which
remedies can be prescribed. It is important not to
have preconceived ideas on causes, nor to jump to
conclusions, otherwise an incorrect remedy may be
put in hand, perhaps more expensive than necessary.
Diagnosis is based on commonsense as much as any
profound knowledge of building technology. House
building is a craft or skill not a high form of technology. Half the secret is understanding and becoming
familiar with the terminology used. It is important to
be able not only to diagnose simple defects and instruct
repairs, but also to recognise and describe those
problems which need expert help and act accordingly.

The first step is to gather information. This can be by
observation (sight, smell, touch or even sound) or
from what the building occupier relates. At this stage
it is important to ask the questions on the left hand
page of the defect sheet in this book. This information
should, as a second step, be related to any other relevant information in the files (specifications, drawings,
maintenance history) and finally passed to the person
responsible for dealing with the defect (surveyor,
maintenance inspector or manager, contractor, maintenance foreman or operative). You will not necessarily
always be involved in all these stages but you should be
aware of them so that the maximum amount of useful
and relevant information can be passed on.

Introduction

The more that can be found about why defects have occurred, the more can be fed back through the maintenance information system to the professionals responsible for the design of new and rehabilitated houses, so that mistakes in design or specifications can be avoided in the future.

CAUSES OF DEFECTS

General causes

Defects occur either because of poor design, or low quality workmanship, or because the building was not constructed according to the design, or because it has been subject to factors not allowed for in the design. These primary causes may operate singly or in combination and result in defects indicated by changes in composition of materials; in the construction itself; in the size, shape or weight of materials or parts of a building; or simply in appearance. The main agents of these changes are:

* Wear and tear
* Applied forces (ground movement, traffic vibration)
* Gases or liquids (dampness, chemical attack)
* Biological agents (rot, mould, fungi)
* Climate or temperature
* Fire.

Simple examples of causes and effects are:

* Poor workmanship in construction could cause penetration of dampness shown up by a damp patch on the wall, the resulting defect which is a change in appearance; or the result could be rot in timber, a change in composition.

* Insufficient attention to foundation design could lead to ground movement indicated by cracks in the brick walls, a change in construction; perhaps also with a sagging roof, a change in shape.

* Not allowing for heavy trolley traffic in the design of a sheltered house could result in wear and tear causing changes in appearance to the floor finishes.

11

Introduction

The reason for giving these examples is to indicate
the way in which a defect arises. A primary cause
allows an agent of change to operate, resulting in the
defect, which is a symptom both of agent and cause.
The main sections of this book describe defects in
detail, but some of the most commonly met defects
are discussed briefly below.

Dampness

Many defects encountered either cause or are caused
by dampness. The cure of dampness is half the battle
in maintenance. If you see a damp patch ask yourself
where the water has come from and deal with the
more obvious possibilities first. There are four general
reasons for dampness; these are condensation, leaking
plumbing, spillage and penetration from the outside.

Condensation is caused in the main by inadequate
heating, insulation and ventilation coupled with excessive moisture production by cooking, bathing, paraffin
heaters and even to some extent breathing. Always
ask about the use of the room concerned, the type of
heating used and the way in which it is used, ie
whether it is intermittently hot and cold or if it has
steady background heat. The cure for condensation
can be a combination of improved insulation and ventilation, but it could also be education of the user.

Leaking plumbing can include appliances, tanks and
pipework, some of which will be in the roof space.
Always check on plumbing above damp patches. The
cure for this problem is to repair the leak, dry out
and redecorate.

When quantities of water are spilled or used for
cleaning, some water may find its way through
floors on to lower ceilings and walls. If there is
a floor above the problem area, always ask if water
has been spilled or used for cleaning. The cure is to
dry the area, redecorate and advise how to avoid
further accidents.

Penetration is the least likely cause of dampness you will encounter and probably the most difficult to diagnose. In older houses it can be due to defective roofing or rainwater gutters and pipes, rain penetrating through the walls, or water drawn up into the structure from the ground (rising damp is the only instance where you may find water has travelled uphill). The cure depends on the exact problem and is best left for the surveyor to decide.

Applied forces and changes in size

A second type of defect commonly encountered is cracked plasterwork to ceilings and walls, or ill-fitting timber components such as doors or window frames. These defects are caused on one hand by swelling and shrinking of various materials as they dry out or become damp, but could, on the other hand, be caused by structural failure such as foundation movement, a much more serious matter. In general, cracks which do not get worse are cured by filling and redecoration; doors and windows which do not fit are eased. Cracks or misfits which suddenly get worse, indicate more serious problems and must be referred to the surveyor.

Defective fittings and installations

A third common defect is a broken or worn out fitting or installation, ranging from a simple item like a door lock or window catch, cases for which you can instruct repair or replacement, to the more complex items, such as electrical systems, boilers and water heaters, for which it is necessary to call in specialist help from an installer or maintenance contractor.

All gas, oil and electrical problems are difficult to diagnose and potentially very dangerous and they must be referred to experts. The lay person should never go beyond checking the setting of controls, the use of the system, possibly replacing blown fuses and assessing whether the user is misusing or over-loading the system.

Introduction

HOW TO USE THIS BOOK

How to find the place you need in this book

(1)   Identify the defective component of the building
        and look up in the contents pages the main sec-
        tion heading A to G, or identify the general
        problem (dampness, defect in appearance or
        defective materials) and look up the main sec-
        tion heading H to K.

(2)   Read through the defects listed under the main
        section heading. If the defect is identified turn
        to the defect sheet (explained below) shown by
        the contents page. If the defect is not clearly
        identified, turn to the key question sheet for
        the main section indicated by the contents page.
        The key question sheet guides you to the
        relevant defect sheet and is particularly useful
        when similar symptoms may derive from essen-
        tially different causes.

(3)   If you are working from the key question sheet,
        ask yourself the questions on the left hand side
        of the sheet; then use the table on the right hand
        side whose columns and rows indicate what and
        where the defect may be. The box where the
        row and the column meet shows the relevant sub-
        section reference, ie the defect sheet you want.

(4)   If you still cannot find the problem, refer to the
        general index at the back which lists the com-
        ponents and defects in alphabetical order.
        However you should bear in mind that a book of
        this size cannot possibly cover all known defects.
        If you are unable to find a description which fits
        the defect you are dealing with, seek more
        experienced advice.

HOW TO USE THE DEFECT SHEETS

Defects are categorised under the general headings
given in the index. Thus Section D, for example,

collects together those defects likely to be encountered in relation to internal walls, ceilings and
finishes. When you have found the correct place in
the book you will see that each defect is dealt with on
a pair of facing pages, together known as a defect
sheet.

On the left hand page, beneath the defect description
and location, are sections showing symptoms, checks
and questions to be asked, and the action you should
take. The symptoms section gives a concise description of what can be seen, felt or smelt. It also
indicates cases where what is seen is only a secondary
feature of a hidden defect. Checks and questions to be
asked are essentially straightforward, pertinent
checks and questions that anyone might sensibly do or
ask. They aim to establish such information as: how
long something has been going wrong. Or, when was
it first noticed? Information resulting from the checks
and questions should be passed on to the surveyor or
person carrying out the repair.

The action section gives an indication of situations
where non-specialists may be able to instruct repairs
themselves and those cases where a technical person
should be brought in. This person is referred to as
'surveyor' although his job title could in reality be
maintenance manager, supervisor, inspector or
consultant.

The right hand page is also divided into sections;
these give the cause of the defect and the remedial
action likely to be needed. Details of causes have
been kept as brief as possible although, in some
cases, they are expanded where there is a natural
sequence of events leading finally to evidence of a
defect. Where there is more than one possible cause
of a defect, these have been numbered; the corres-
ponding remedial action is then similarly numbered.
Descriptions of remedies indicate what are sometimes
multiple tasks carried out by other people. The aim of
this section is to give you some idea of what is involved.
This is particularly important where it may be neces-

sary to let occupants know of the likely inconvenience to them in putting right the defect. However you should remember that causes of defects are often complex and the remedies listed in this book are fairly simplistic in order to give an idea of the type of solution to the problem. At the foot of the right hand page are <u>cross references</u> to other defect sheets, to relevant page numbers in Part I of the NBA's Maintenance Training package on House Construction and to the slides issued by the NBA in Part III.

EXAMPLE OF USE OF THIS BOOK

Let us consider a short anecdote to show how use of the booklet might work in practice. Henry or Henrietta Allen (HA), a housing assistant in a small association working in an inner city area, is called to visit Ted and Edna Newton (TEN), tenants who have complained that their central heating is not working properly.

HA reaches the address, opens the pocket book to the contents page, finds a reference to radiators under Section F, turns to key question sheet F, and knocks on the door. HA listens to detailed complaints of frozen tenants while observing that the system con-sists of radiators with a gas-fired boiler in the kitchen. HA sees from key question sheet F that boilers and radiators are on defect sheets F10 and F11 and so turns to these.

HA takes first F10, the boiler, and runs through the 'Checks/questions' (bottom of left page). Everything seems to be in order so HA is directed by the box 'Other defects' (bottom of right page) F11, which covers radiators. HA establishes from questioning the TEN that the radiators in the kitchen and bathroom are fine but the bedroom and lounge radiators are only lukewarm and the hall is cold. HA goes through F11 'Checks/questions' but cannot make the circulatory pump start when it should. Is this a job for the heating engineer? No, not necessarily. HA sees from F11

'Causes' (top right) that the electrical supply may have
fused and so replaces the fuse in the pump circuit (fuses
are marked inside the lid of the consumer unit and HA
always carries a few spares); the pump starts. HA
feels good and accepts the offer of a cup of tea while
waiting to check if all the radiators heat up properly.

The TEN starts normal social pleasantries; HA exp-
lains the job and shows this pocket book, whereupon
TEN says, "While you are here we have just thought of
something else we think you ought to check". HA is
led to the upstairs front bedroom and shown a yellowy-
brown stain on the ceiling and on the top of the wall at
the front of the room. HA detects a damp smell and
opens the pocket book at contents page to find Section
H 'DAMPNESS'. HA turns to the key question sheet H
and asks if the patch gets worse when it is raining or
generally just in damp weather. The answer is that
damp is associated with rain, and this coupled with
the location of the damp patch at the ceiling and top
of the wall below the roof, guides HA to defect sheets
H8, H9 and H10. The roof, seen from outside, is flat
but does not have a parapet. This cuts out H8 (parapets)
and H10 (pitched roofs) but leaves H9 (dampness to
underside of flat roofs). All of these problems must be
referred to the surveyor, but HA must note as much
information as possible to help him. HA goes through
the H9 'Checks/questions' (bottom left) and notes the
name, address, telephone number, access availability,
nature of problem, type of house and answers to the
'Checks/questions' on a standard maintenance request
form used by the association, for reference to the
surveyor. HA then advises the TEN that the surveyor
will call to assess necessary repairs to roof and
decorations. HA returns to base with the feeling of
another good job done - one simple defect rectified and
another potentially serious defect caught in time and
under control.

EXTERNAL WALLS AND CHIMNEYS

The figures in the boxes on the opposite page are the reference numbers of the defect sheets which explain how to deal with the defects.

Questions to ask which will lead you to the correct defect sheet:

WHAT IS THE DEFECT ?

IS IT IN EXTERNAL WALL BRICKWORK ?

IS IT IN CHIMNEY BRICKWORK ?

IS IT IN RENDERING TO EXTERNAL BRICKWORK ?

IS IT IN RENDERING TO CHIMNEY BRICKWORK ?

A

	WHERE IS THE DEFECT?			A
WHAT IS THE DEFECT?	Brickwork of an external wall	Brickwork of a chimney	Render to brickwork of an external wall	Render to brickwork of a chimney
Cracking and splitting	A1 A3	A2 A3	A8 A7	A7 A8
Bending, bulging and bowing	A1 A5	A2		
Crumbling mortar	A3	A2 A3		
Crumbling bricks	A4	A4		
Movement of bricks at dpc	A1 A5	A5		
Flaking of rendering			A6	A2 A6
Defective paint-work			A9	A9

EXTERNAL WALLS AND CHIMNEYS

	CRACKED BRICKWORK
Location	External walls
Symptoms	Horizontal, vertical and diagonal cracks can be seen running along, down or across external walls and may be accompanied by overhanging of brickwork at dpc level and/or bowing of the wall.
Checks/ questions	* Has the crack moved over a period of time; ie has it become wider or longer? * Is there adjacent building development? * Is mining carried out in the area? * Has the weather been abnormally wet or dry? * Is there a tree close to the wall, or has one recently been felled?
Action	Refer to surveyor.

Defect	CRACKED BRICKWORK	A1
Location	External walls	
Causes	Cracks may be caused by any of the following: * Subsoil movement (including change of water content) * Foundation movement and failure * Expansion of brickwork * Chemical action on brickwork * Failure of wall ties * Spread of the roof structure (ie pushing out the walls).	
Remedies	Stable cracks: Fill with a compressible filler which prevents water penetration and allows for further movement. The tenant can remain whilst repairs are carried out. Unstable cracks are structural defects and may involve excavation, underpinning and rebuilding parts of walls. This may involve temporary rehousing.	

Cross references	Part I page no	Part II other defect sheet references		Part III slide no
	14	A5	E1	1
		B3		2
		D1		3

Defect	CRACKING, SPLITTING AND BENDING OF CHIMNEY STACKS
Location	Chimneys
Symptoms	Symptoms could include cracking of mortar joints, vertical splitting, bending and distortion of the stack, cracking of rendering, displacement of the chimney pot, damp or stained areas, displaced parging falling within stack.
Checks/ questions	* Have the chimney checked for structural stability. * What appliance does the chimney stack serve? * Are there any signs of dampness on the plasterwork?
Action	Refer to surveyor.

Defect	CRACKING, SPLITTING AND BENDING OF CHIMNEY STACKS	A2
Location	Chimneys	

Causes	This defect is usually due to condensation of the water vapour in the flue gases, particularly above roof level. Condensed water migrates into the stack which may then tend to crack. Water passes through the cracks possibly reaching the plaster.
	Note that the defect may be more pronounced with stacks serving slow combustion solid fuel appliances.

Remedies	Where the stack is bent or mortar joints are in poor condition, dismantle and rebuild the stack with a lining to prevent seepage of condensed water.
	If the stack has not been badly affected it might be possible to line the chimney without rebuilding it.

Cross references	Part I page no	Part II other defect sheet references		Part III slide no
	15	A3	A7	4
		A4	A8	5
		A6	H7	

Defect	CRUMBLING OF BRICKWORK MORTAR JOINTS
Location	External walls and chimneys
Symptoms	Mortar seems soft and crumbling in the joints, particularly after cold weather. Cracks may appear along the horizontal joints. Brickwork may absorb moisture, shown by damp patches.
Checks/ questions	* What is the extent of the soft mortar? * Are there definite horizontal lines of defective mortar? * How long ago was the building completed? * Did a particularly cold spell occur before the defective mortar was first seen? * Is water leaking on to joints?
Action	Refer to surveyor.

Defect	CRUMBLING OF BRICKWORK MORTAR JOINTS	A3
Location	External walls and chimneys	
Causes	1 Incorrect mortar mixture. 2 Frost action. 3 Where definite cracking occurs along the horizontal joints, it is likely that chemical action is the cause. 4 Leaking gutter or rainwater pipe.	
Remedies	1 Rebuild in severe cases. If the extent of soft and crumbling mortar is limited repoint the joint. 2 Repoint with a stronger mortar than was originally used. 3 Prevent water from entering the wall by rendering, cladding or the application of water repellants. 4 Repair or replace the gutter or rainwater pipe.	

Cross references	Part I page no	Part II other defect sheet references	Part III slide no
	14	A2 B7 A7 B6	6

Defect	CRUMBLING OF BRICKS
Location	External walls and chimneys
Symptoms	Some bricks crumble on the surface and are visibly recessed back from the rest.
Checks/ questions	* Has crumbling been occurring over a long period? * Is the wall particularly exposed to severe weather conditions?
Action	Refer to surveyor.

Defect	CRUMBLING OF BRICKS	A4

Location	External walls and chimneys

Causes	Frost action, chemical action or combination of both.

Remedies	Where only a few bricks are affected, cut out and replace them or alternatively render the wall. Where the action is extensive the outer brick leaf could be renewed. However, it is often more economic to cover the existing brickwork with a weather screen such as tile hanging or ship-lap boarding to prevent water penetration and subsequent frost and chemical action.

Cross references	Part I page no	Part II other defect sheet references	Part III slide no
	14	A2	7

Defect	MOVEMENT OF BRICKWORK INCLUDING SQUEEZING OUT OF DAMP-PROOF COURSE
Location	External walls and chimneys
Symptoms	This defect shows either as outward bulging of the wall, or, where the wall is long, as an over-sailing at the end of the wall.
Checks/ questions	* Has movement definitely taken place? * Is there any forcing out of the damp-proof course material? * Is the wall obviously bowed at all? * Have any cracks resulted from bowing? * Is the mortar in the joints cracked, soft or breaking away?
Action	Refer to surveyor.

Defect	MOVEMENT OF BRICKWORK INCLUDING SQUEEZING OUT OF DAMP-PROOF COURSE	A5
Location	External walls and chimneys	

Causes	The main causes are moisture expansion of the brickwork and chemical action coupled with the lack of cohesion of the damp-proof course.
	'Spread' or other movement of roof structure may also cause walls to go out of plumb, which will appear as a bulge outwards at the top of the wall.

Remedies	For a building, action is seldom necessary. For an unstable boundary wall junction rebuild the corners with an expansion joint.

Cross references	Part I page no	Part II other defect sheet references	Part III slide no
	16	A2	8
	17	K5	

Defect	FLAKING OF RENDERING ON BRICKWORK
Location	External walls and chimneys
Symptoms	Top coat splits away from the undercoat, sometimes taking with it a thin film of undercoat.
Checks/ questions	* How extensive is the defect ? * Has the undercoat come away with the top coat ? * How long ago was the rendering last painted ?
Action	Instruct repair.

Defect	FLAKING OF RENDERING ON BRICKWORK	A6
Location	External walls and chimneys	
Causes	Differential shrinkage of top and bottom coats.	
Remedies	If only small areas are affected, remove loose material, roughen undercoat and apply top coat. If necessary, treat the undercoat with a bonding agent before applying the top coat. Where extensive, the whole top coat may have to be replaced.	

Cross references	Part I page no	Part II other defect sheet references	Part III slide no
	14	A2	9

Defects	HORIZONTAL CRACKING OF RENDERING ON BRICKWORK
Location	External walls and chimneys
Symptoms	Horizontal cracking along the lines of the brick-work joints underneath.
Checks/ questions	* Do cracks in rendering match brickwork joints? * Is there any sign of an increase in the height of the external leaf of the wall? * Is the wall becoming wetter than normal?
Action	Refer to surveyor.

Defect	HORIZONTAL CRACKING OF RENDERING ON BRICKWORK	A7
Location	External walls and chimneys	
Causes	Chemical action causes the mortar joints to expand upwards, causing rendering to crack.	
Remedies	Extensive cracking is difficult to make good without total renewal of rendering. It is essential to prevent water penetration. Some form of weather cladding such as ship-lap boarding or tile hanging is the most likely solution.	

Cross references	Part I page no	Part II other defect sheet references	Part III slide no
	14	A3	10

Defect	RANDOM CRACKING OF RENDERING ON BRICKWORK
Location	External walls and chimneys
Symptoms	Cracks forming no definite pattern are seen. When tapped, the rendering in the vicinity of the crack may sound hollow whilst in some places, it may have fallen away.
Checks/ questions	* Do cracks correspond to any cracks in the brickwork? * Does rendering sound hollow when tapped? * How long has rendering been on the wall?
Action	Refer to surveyor.

Defect	RANDOM CRACKING OF RENDERING ON BRICKWORK	A8
Location	External walls and chimneys	

Causes	1 Cracks resulting directly from cracks in the brickwork.
	2 Shrinkage of cement-based rendering causing cracks and penetration of water. Chemical action may also affect the back facing of the rendering resulting in cracking and falling off.

Remedies	1 Repair cracks in brickwork and then make good the rendering.
	2 Extensive cracking and break away is difficult to make good without total re-rendering which is costly. To prevent water penetration and chemical attack, weather cladding such as tile hanging or ship-lap boarding is necessary. Painting with a cement-based paint or a textured coating may help.

Cross references	Part I page no	Part II other defect sheet references	Part III slide no
	14	A2	11

Defect	BLISTERING OF PAINTWORK TO RENDERING AND CLADDING
Location	External walls and chimneys
Symptoms	Blisters or bubbles forming early in the life of buildings may contain water. In older buildings the paint film may have cracked and peeled back. Efflorescent salts may also be seen.
Checks/ questions	* Do the blisters contain liquid or are they dry? * If dry, do the blisters contain any signs of efflorescence?
Action	Refer to surveyor.

Defect	BLISTERING OF PAINTWORK TO RENDERING AND CLADDING	A9
Location	External walls and chimneys	
Causes	1 Water from rendering which has not had adequate time to dry out. 2 Chemical attack on the paint film.	
Remedies	Eliminate all sources of water and redecorate.	

Cross references	Part I page no	Part II other defect sheet references	Part III slide no
	15	J2	12

The figures in the boxes on the opposite page are the reference numbers of the defect sheets which explain how to deal with the defects.

Questions to ask which will lead you to the correct defect sheet:

WHAT IS THE DEFECT?

IS THE ROOF FLAT OR PITCHED?

WHAT IS THE ROOF COVERING MATERIAL?

B

WHAT IS THE DEFECT?	WHERE IS THE DEFECT?			**B**
	Asphalt surfaced flat roof	Felt surfaced flat roof	Tiled pitched roof	Slated pitched roof
Blistering or rippling of roof covering	B1	B2		
Splitting and cracking of roof covering	B1	B2		
Sagging and deformation			B3	B3
Surface deterioration including slipped slates or tiles			B4	B5
Leaking gutters	B6	B6	B6	B6
Blocked or leaking rainwater pipe	B7	B7	B7	B7

ROOFS, GUTTERS AND RAINWATER PIPES

Defect	BLISTERING, SPLITTING AND CRACKING OF ASPHALT ROOF SURFACES
Location	Flat roofs
Symptoms	Broken blisters, splits or cracks seen in roof covering which may have allowed water to penetrate to roof structure.
Checks/ questions	* If blisters are present, have any of them broken? * Are there any damp patches on the ceiling immediately below the flat roof that correspond to broken blisters, splits or cracks? * Is there any obvious disturbance to the adjacent wall or parapet? * How long since roof was surfaced?
Action	Refer to surveyor.

Defect	BLISTERING, SPLITTING AND CRACKING OF ASPHALT ROOF SURFACES	B1

Location	Flat roofs

Causes	**Blistering** 1 Water trapped when the roof was laid may vaporise and force up the asphalt. 2 Water from condensation of water vapour passing into the roof structure from the room below may force up the asphalt. **Splitting and cracking** 3 Asphalt is past its useful life. 4 The base on which the asphalt is laid may have moved.

Remedies	1 Open up fully, dry out and repair the surface. 2 As above. However, consideration should also be given to the provision of barrier to prevent water vapour passing into the roof structure. 3 Full replacement. 4 A surveyor may decide to convert a split to a flexible joint to allow for any future movement.

Cross references	Part I page no	Part II other defect sheet references	Part III slide no
	19	H8 H9	13

Defect	BLISTERING, SPLITTING AND RIPPLING OF BITUMEN FELT ROOF SURFACES
Location	Flat roofs
Symptoms	Blistered, split and rippled areas may be seen on flat roof surfaces. Where blisters have broken, water may have penetrated. The sliding effect of one felt layer over another might have accelerated the entry of water. Distinct splits are also obvious sources of penetration.
Checks/ questions	* If blisters are present, have any of them broken? * Is the ceiling of the room immediately below the roof showing any signs of dampness? * Is there any obvious disturbance to the adjacent wall or parapet? Note that damp patches may not correspond to obvious defects in the roof surface as water can enter and travel horizontally between felt layers before appearing as dampness.
Action	Refer to surveyor.

Defect	BLISTERING, SPLITTING AND RIPPLING OF BITUMEN FELT ROOF SURFACES	B2

Location	Flat roofs

Causes	Many defects result directly from poor quality felt and/or inadequate attention to laying it.

Blistering

1 Mainly due to the expansion of air or vapour-isation of water trapped between the layers when the felt was laid.

2 The water may have derived from condensation of water vapour which has passed into the structure from the room below.

Splitting and rippling

3 Mainly due to the base on which felting was laid, having moved.

4 Roof surface is past its useful life.

Remedies	

1 Where defects have not led to leakage, no immediate action is required other than subsequent regular checks. However, it is advisable to release trapped water and allow the roof to dry out before repairing it.

2 As above. Consideration should also be given to preventing water vapour passing into the roof structure from the room below by providing a vapour barrier.

3 A surveyor may decide to convert a split into a flexible joint to allow for any future movement.

4 Replace the roof surface.

Cross references	Part I page no	Part II other defect sheet references	Part III slide no
	19	H8	14
		H9	15

Defect	SAGGING AND DEFORMATION
Location	Pitched roofs
Symptoms	The roof may sag and in severe cases, cracks may be present in the top courses of brickwork immediately under the eaves. These top courses may also have moved outwards or the wall may have moved out of plumb.
Checks/ questions	* Ascertain if the roof has ever been retiled or reslated. If so is the present covering heavier than the original ? * Is there any sign of woodworm or fungal attack in timbers in the roof space ?
Action	Refer to surveyor.

Defect	SAGGING AND DEFORMATION	B3
Location	Pitched roofs	

Causes	1 Overloaded or inadequate timbers.
	2 Beetle or fungal attack.
	3 Dry rot.

Remedies	1 The roof can be strengthened by adding timber members. Remedial action may not be necessary unless the roof becomes unstable. Continued observation is important. Where the roof cladding is too heavy it may be necessary to replace it with a lighter one.
	2 } The presence of woodworm or fungal growths 3 } must be treated and this may involve the replacement of various timbers.

Cross references	Part I page no	Part II other defect sheet references	Part III slide no
	18	K1 K2 K3	16

Defect	DETERIORATING AND SLIPPING ROOF TILES
Location	Pitched roofs
Symptoms	Tiles may show signs of surface deterioration. Initially only a few may be defective but in time larger areas become affected. Some tiles may have slipped.
	If leakage occurs, it may show as damp patches on ceilings.
Checks/ questions	* How old are the tiles?
	* Is the roof pitch steep or shallow?
	* Is there any apparent dampness present in the roof space areas or on upstairs ceilings?
	* How extensive is the defect; ie is it over small or large areas?
Action	Instruct repair where single tiles or small areas require repair. Otherwise refer to surveyor.

Defect	DETERIORATING AND SLIPPING ROOF TILES	B4
Location	Pitched roofs	

Causes	Surface deterioration is primarily due to frost action. Since this is associated with the presence of water, tiles on roofs of relatively shallow pitch may be susceptible. Tile slippage occurs because the fixing no longer holds; ie the nibs of tiles have disintegrated or the wooden pegs may have shrunk and dropped out.

Remedies	Replace small areas of tiles. This presents no problems, but complete replacement will be necessary sooner or later; this should be considered as an initial solution where there are large areas of defect. Replacement tiles should be of a type having good frost resistance.

Cross references	Part I page no	Part II other defect sheet references	Part III slide no
	18 19	H10	17

Defect	DETERIORATING AND SLIPPING ROOF SLATES
Location	Pitched roofs
Symptoms	Pieces of slate may have broken off and slippage may have occurred. Leakage into the roof space may show by dampness on ceilings.
Checks/ questions	* Is the air in the vicinity known to be polluted? * Is there any apparent dampness present in the roof space area or on upstairs ceilings?
Action	Instruct repair where single slates or small areas are affected. Otherwise refer to surveyor.

Defect	DETERIORATING AND SLIPPING ROOF SLATES	B5
Location	Pitched roofs	

| Causes | The principal cause of <u>deteriorating slates</u> is attack by polluted air. A rarer cause is frost attack.

<u>Slipping</u> occurs for a number of reasons:

1 The nail holes in the slate are still intact but the actual nail has rusted away.

2 The nail holes have broken. This is normally an indication of general slate deterioration and may be aggravated by corroding nails.

3 The battens to which the slates are attached have been weakened by either fungal attack or woodworm.

4 Slates have been accidentally displaced. |
|---|---|

| Remedies | 1 ⎫
2 ⎭ It is easy to replace individual or small areas of slates, but corrosion may continue. It may be advisable to strip the whole roof and refix slates using nails resistant to corrosion.

3 Replace damaged battens after conditions favourable to fungal or woodworm attack have been corrected.

4 Replace displaced slates. |
|---|---|

Cross references	Part I page no	Part II other defect sheet references	Part III slide no
	18 19	H10	18

Defect	LEAKING GUTTERS
Location	Gutters
Symptoms	Water may leak or overflow from points along the guttering. In some cases, it may cause dampness on external and internal surfaces.
Checks/ questions	* Is the leakage from an overflow of the gutter or an apparent hole, slit or defective joint? * Has the guttering recently been replaced? * Is the roof water flowing into the gutter? * Is the gutter water flowing into the downpipes? * Is the downpipe blocked or leaking? * How old is the guttering? * Is the guttering made of cast iron, galvanised steel, asbestos or plastic? * What is the defective guttering dripping or leaking on to?
Action	Instruct repair if cause 1; otherwise refer to surveyor.

Defect	LEAKING GUTTERS	B6

Location	Gutters

Causes	1 Gutters are blocked so that water collects and overflows. A downpipe may be blocked so that water 'backs up' into the gutters.
	2 Guttering is old and becomes perforated or joints are no longer effective.
	3 Guttering may be new but wrongly positioned so as not to catch water flowing off roofs, or it may be sloped the wrong way to flow to downpipes. Joints may also have been incorrectly made.
	4 Heat from a nearby flue may have deformed the gutter.

Remedies	1 Unblock, checking that guttering is not perforated or joints are bad.
	2 Where the guttering is extensively defective, it all has to be replaced. Isolated holes and defective joints in downpipes can be individually repaired.
	3 Reposition guttering such that gutters function normally. Remake any faulty joints.
	4 Protect gutter from heat of flue or replace with asbestos cement-type.

Cross references	Part I page no	Part II other defect sheet references	Part III slide no
	20	H3 K4 H8 H10	19

Defect	BLOCKED OR LEAKING RAINWATER PIPES
Location	External wall
Symptoms	Water fills the blocked pipe so the gutter eventually overflows. Stains and discolouration may occur on the leaking pipe around joints or on wall behind pipe or gutter. Moss, fungus or even plants may grow from joints or damaged section of pipe.
Checks/ questions	* Is the gutter overflowing at the top of pipe? * Is the pipe or wall behind the pipe damp or stained? * Is the pipe obviously damaged or dislocated? * Has an adjacent climbing plant found its way into a joint?
Action	Instruct clearance if cause 1 or 2; otherwise refer to surveyor.

Defect	BLOCKED OR LEAKING RAINWATER PIPES	B7
Location	External wall	

Causes	1 Pipe is blocked by leaves, bird nest materials or general rubbish entering from gutter.
	2 Pipe is blocked by plant growth entering through joints.
	3 Pipe is cracked through corrosion or impact by vehicle or heavy article.
	4 Pipe has been displaced through impact (resting ladder against it, children playing) and leaks at its joints.
Remedies	1 Rod pipe to clear it; clean out gutter and fit pipe guard in top of rainwater pipe to prevent re-occurrence.
	2 Remove plant growth; rod pipe to clear it.
	3 Replace or repair damaged pipe section.
	4 Refix pipe in position, using extra clips where necessary to prevent re-occurrence, and remake the joints.

Cross references	Part I page no	Part II other defect sheet references	Part III slide no
	20	H3 J3	19

WINDOWS, DOORS AND EXTERNAL JOINERY

The figures in the boxes on the opposite page are the reference numbers of the defect sheets which explain how to deal with the defects.

Questions to ask which will lead you to the correct defect sheet:

WHAT IS THE DEFECT?

DOES IT AFFECT JOINERY GENERALLY?

DOES IT PARTICULARLY AFFECT WINDOWS?

DOES IT AFFECT WOOD OR METAL FRAMED WINDOWS?

DOES IT AFFECT DOORS?

C

WHAT IS THE DEFECT?	WHERE IS THE DEFECT?			C
	Generally in joinery	Specifically in timber framed windows	Specifically in metal framed windows	Specifically in timber doors
Surface deterioration	C1			C5
Timber decay	C1 C2			
Paintwork deterioration including flaking and peeling	C1			
Cracked or missing putty	C2		C4	
Distortion (of shape)		C3	C4	C6
Rusting			C4	
Cracked glass			C4	

WINDOWS, DOORS AND EXTERNAL JOINERY

Defect	TIMBER DECAY
Location	Windows, doors and external joinery
Symptoms	Flat timber surfaces seem to be deformed and underlying areas are soft and break off easily. Paintwork may be discoloured. The deformation is particularly noticeable if comparison is made between affected and unaffected areas.
Checks/ questions	* Is the woodwork soft and friable? * Have the joints opened up? * Has the putty shrunk away from the glazing? * Is the sealant between joinery and brickwork loose? * Is the paintwork discoloured or flaking? * When was the woodwork last painted?
Action	Refer to surveyor.

Defect	TIMBER DECAY	C1
Location	Windows, doors and external joinery	
Causes	The decay is due to wood-destroying fungus, usually wet rot. Untreated timber which has become fairly wet is ideal for such growth. Water is likely to have entered via open joints, defective putty and other defects in joinery which have been badly maintained; it may have been trapped when the window was painted during wet weather, or it may come from wet walls in contact with the window.	
Remedies	For localised attack, cut away the affected area and fit a new piece of wood suitably treated with preservative. Strip all adjacent paintwork, allow wood to dry, brush with preservative and repaint. If decay is extensive it is advisable to replace all affected components. Where the general condition of joinery is poor due to lack of maintenance, old and failed putty should be removed and the paintwork stripped and primed. Fill all holes and joints with a water-insoluble filler, re-putty and repaint.	

Cross references	Part I page no	Part II other defect sheet references	Part III slide no
	25	K1 K2	20

Defect	DETERIORATION OF PAINTWORK AND PUTTY
Location	Windows, doors and external joinery
Symptoms	Flaking or peeling paintwork. Loose, cracked or missing putty. Soft timber.
Checks/ questions	* Is the paintwork flaking? * Has the woodwork been previously primed? Check this by examining the back of paint flakes. * Does any wood adhere to flakes of paint which are examined? * Have the joints opened up? * Has the putty shrunk away from the glazing? * Is the sealant between joinery and brickwork surface loose?
Action	Instruct repair.

Defect	DETERIORATION OF PAINTWORK AND PUTTY	C2
Location	Windows, doors and external joinery	
Causes	This defect is due to age or lack of maintenance. Paintwork also fails because of lack of adhesion due to moisture or because moisture has caused excessive frame movement. The moisture may result from having been trapped when previous repainting was carried out in wet weather or by movement from brickwork adjacent to the joinery.	
Remedies	Where a small amount of paintwork is defective, strip back, rub down and make good. In extreme cases, strip all paintwork and putty, replace glass, re-prime and repaint. Paint can be stripped with a chemical stripper or by being burnt off with a blowlamp and scraper. Where the joints are defective, strip out defective putty or sealant and make good.	

Cross references	Part I page no	Part II other defect sheet references	Part III slide no
	24 25	C3 K5	21

Defect	DISTORTION OF TIMBER WINDOWS
Location	Windows
Symptoms	Distorted joinery and consequent gaps, lack of fit and draughts.
Checks/ questions	* Are windows distorted? * Are there gaps when the window is closed? * Do thick paint runs prevent the proper closing of the window? * Is the window a source of air for heating appliances? * Have the joints opened up (and possibly been filled) resulting in the window sticking in the frame?
Action	Instruct repair of obvious defects. Refer to surveyor if window supplies air to heating appliance.

Defect	DISTORTION OF TIMBER WINDOWS	C3

Location	Windows

Causes	1 Woodwork not regularly painted is subject to varying moisture contents which cause expansion and contraction. 2 Uneven application of paint can lead to poor fit. 3 Where a window is the source of air for heating appliances, the amount of air drawn in through the window is considerable resulting in excessive draughts. 4 New window frames may have been put in old sub-frames, resulting in poor fit after shrinkage. 5 Joints have opened up.

Remedies	1 Repair distorted window joinery, or in extreme cases replace it. 2 Correct surface defects. 3 An alternative source of air for the appliance might be possible. If not, the air requirement of the appliance might be reduced by fitting a throat restrictor. The window could then be partially weatherstripped, reducing draughts. 4 Fill gaps with jointing compound or cover with draught proofing strips or tape. 5 Clean out joint, apply epoxy resin glue, and place in cramps until glue has set.

Cross references	Part I page no	Part II other defect sheet references	Part III slide no
	23 24	C2	

Defect	CRACKING OF GLASS IN STEEL WINDOWS
Location	Windows
Symptoms	Glass in steel window frames is cracked. The frames are generally old and often rusting. Putty may also be partially defective. In severe cases distortion of the frame may have occurred.
Checks/ questions	* Is the frame rusted ? * Has the putty lifted out of its original position ? * Is the frame distorted ?
Action	Instruct repair but refer to surveyor if frame is distorted or severely rusted.

Defect	CRACKING OF GLASS IN STEEL WINDOWS	C4
Location	Windows	

Causes	The main cause of cracking is rusting of the steel framework which was insufficiently protected prior to use. This is characteristic of all steel window frames used before 1940. As rusting takes place it expands the frame, exerting pressure on the glass which cracks. Rusting may be caused by rainwater finding its way down the back edge of external glazing putties or, condensed water seeping down and between window pane and frame.
Remedies	Remove putty, glass and excess rust, treat the steel with rust inhibitor and primer and reglaze the window. Where the frame is badly rusted it may be more economic to renew it. Loose putties in other frames where the glass is still intact can be raked or chipped out and any rust treated but this usually offers only a temporary cure.

Cross references	Part I page no	Part II other defect sheet references	Part III slide no
	24	K4	

Defect	EXTERNAL DELAMINATION OF PLYWOOD PANELS
Location	Doors or external panels
Symptoms	The outer ply of the door or panel is wrinkled and becoming detached from the main part of the panel. Where the entire door or panel is ply, the top ply may be broken or in severe cases all plies may have split open at the edges. Paintwork is inevitably in poor condition.
Checks/ questions	* Is the surface of the door or panel wrinkled ? * What is the state of paintwork ? * What is the condition of the door at its edges, particularly the bottom edge ?
Action	Instruct repair; if severe damage, refer to surveyor.

Defect	EXTERNAL DELAMINATION OF PLYWOOD PANELS	C5
Location	Doors or external panels	
Causes	The defect is likely where external quality plywood has not been used or where paintwork has not provided adequate protection. Bottom edges of doors are particularly vulnerable, especially where joints have opened up.	
Remedies	If the panel has been extensively damaged, replace the door. Otherwise repair, ensuring that all joints have been filled prior to repainting. The addition of a properly fixed weatherboard will deflect water away from the base of a door.	

Cross references	Part I page no	Part II other defect sheet references	Part III slide no
	21	C6	22

Defect	DISTORTION OF TIMBER DOORS
Location	Doors
Symptoms	The door may be warped or swollen so that it no longer fits flush against the door frame, or it may be 'out-of-square' and catch against the frame or threshold, or both symptoms may be evident.
Checks/ questions	* Is the door badly distorted ? * Are there any cracks in the paintwork especially at joints ? * Are there any major differences in temperature or humidity between each side of the door ?
Action	Instruct repair; refer to surveyor if severe distortion.

Defect	DISTORTION OF TIMBER DOORS	C6

Location	Doors

Causes	1 The main cause is changing moisture content of the timber which leads to expansion and contraction. The extent will depend on timber type and grain direction. 2 Distortion also occurs when there are large differences in atmospheric conditions on opposite sides of the door. 3 'Out-of-squareness' usually results from a combination of dry conditions and poorly made joints.

Remedies	1 Where distortion is excessive the only solution may be to replace the door. Alternatively, where distortion is not excessive, fix a weatherboard across the bottom of an external door. 2 Reduce, if possible, any large differences in atmospheric conditions. 3 Plane off the area which is binding (catching). Where the joint is loose, run an epoxy resin adhesive into it to make it more rigid. Repaint the planed area.

Cross references	Part I page no	Part II other defect sheet references	Part III slide no
	21	C5 D10	

The figures on the opposite page are the reference numbers of the defect sheets which explain how to deal with the defects.

Questions to ask which will lead you to the correct defect sheet:

WHAT IS THE DEFECT?

IS IT APPARENT ON THE WALLS AND/OR CEILINGS?

IS IT IN THE APPLIED DECORATION?

IS IT IN THE JOINERY OR DOORS?

D

| WHAT IS THE DEFECT? | WHERE IS THE DEFECT? | | D |
	Walls and/or ceilings	Applied decorations	Joinery and doors
Cracking	D1 D3 D2		
Full thickness of plaster loose	D4		
Top coat of plaster loose	D5		
Pitted plaster	D6		
Discoloured or blistered decorations		D7	
Peeling or flaking paintwork		D11	
Loose tiles		D8	
Surfaces peeling off joinery			D9
Faulty doors			D10

FINISHES TO INTERNAL WALLS, CEILINGS AND JOINERY; INTERNAL DOORS

Defect	CRACKS RELATED TO MOVEMENT IN THE BUILDING STRUCTURE
Location	Walls and ceilings
Symptoms	Cracks which correspond to cracks in the background structure which can be deep and wide, probably with accompanying cracks or bulges on the external face of the building.
Checks/ questions	* Have the cracks shown further movement in the immediate past, ie become wider and/or longer? * Are any structural alterations in progress or have any been recently completed? * Is adjacent building work in progress? * Is mining carried out in the area? * Has the weather been exceptionally wet or dry? * Is there a large tree close by, or has one recently been removed?
Action	Refer to surveyor.

Defect	CRACKS RELATED TO MOVEMENT IN THE BUILDING STRUCTURE	D1
Location	Walls and ceilings	

Causes	1 Movement of foundations due to change in the moisture content of the subsoil, especially shrinkable clays. Subsidence may occur in very dry weather, especially if the roots of trees extend under the foundations; there will be some compensating movement on the return of wet conditions.
	2 Continuing structural movement due to mining activity, chemical attack on the foundations, disturbance of the ground due to adjacent building work or failure of the original structure. (Structural alterations may also give rise to movement if full precautions are not taken.)
	3 Structural movement now stabilised, originally due to initial settlement, former mining activity, etc.

Remedies	1 Wait for cracks to stabilise, fill with flexible filler/sealant.
	2 Urgent action may be necessary by way of shoring, underpinning and structural repairs, perhaps accompanied by evacuation of tenants.
	3 Fill cracks, redecorate.

Cross references	Part I page no	Part II other defect sheet references	Part III slide no
	15 26	A1 D4 D2 D3	23

Defect	SHRINKAGE CRACKS
Location	Walls and ceilings
Symptoms	Cracks which may be long, but only fine, and which appear as new work dries out ie during the first year after completion. They will usually appear at the junctions of floors/walls/ceilings, and may also outline the joints of plasterboard sheets or blockwork background.
Checks/ questions	* Are the cracks associated with recently completed work ? * When were the works completed ? * Has central heating recently been installed ?
Action	Instruct repair.

Defect	SHRINKAGE CRACKS	D2
Location	Walls and ceilings	
Causes	Timber shrinks as it dries, and cement-based products such as in-situ concrete or walling blocks shrink on curing (maturing). As a result new building work may suffer from shrinkage of its components, which shows as cracking at joints and junctions.	
Remedies	Allow time for the drying out process to be completed (about six months), fill the cracks, redecorate.	

	Part I page no	Part II other defect sheet references		Part III slide no
Cross references	26 27	D1 D3 D4	D5 D8	24

Defects	CRACKS ASSOCIATED WITH DIFFERENTIAL MOVEMENT
Location	Walls and ceilings
Symptoms	Cracks may occur at the junction of two different materials or forms of construction in the background structure. These junctions may not be apparent but typically occur at the intersection of internal and external walls, and walls and ceilings. These cracks are not exclusive to new work, and may vary with environmental conditions.
Checks/ questions	* Where do the cracks occur? * Have the cracks varied over time? * How much movement has been observed and under what circumstances?
Action	Refer to surveyor.

Defects	CRACKS ASSOCIATED WITH DIFFERENTIAL MOVEMENT	D3
Location	Walls and ceilings	

Causes	Materials respond differently to changes in humidity and temperature. As a result, where dissimilar materials or forms of construction are used in adjacent parts of the building, differential movement may occur with changing conditions, causing cracks at the junction. Differential movement may also arise from varying conditions which occur in different parts of the structure, for example, external walls are subject to thermal movement.

Remedies	It is inadvisable to fill such cracks with rigid material. Where significant movement occurs, some form of sliding cover strip or flexible joint may be necessary, otherwise it might be adequate to cover with lining paper. At wall/ceiling junctions a cornice (fixed only either to the wall or to the ceiling if necessary) will hide wide cracks.

Cross references	Part I page no	Part II other defect sheet references		Part III slide no
	26	D1	D5	
	27	D2	D8	
		D4		

Defect	FULL THICKNESS OF PLASTER LOOSE
Location	Walls and ceilings
Symptoms	The full thickness of plaster has come away from the background; loose areas sound hollow when tapped, and cracks will often be evident. The plaster may bulge or sag, and in extreme cases, will have fallen away.
Checks/ questions	* How old is the plaster? * Are cracks recent or longstanding? * What is the background material? * What is the extent of hollowness? * How much plaster has fallen away, or appears to be likely to fall?
Action	Refer to surveyor.

Defect	FULL THICKNESS OF PLASTER LOOSE	D4
Location	Walls and ceilings	

Causes	1 Plaster has failed to adhere to a dense concrete background, probably due to the use of an unsuitable undercoat.
	2 Plaster has broken away from timber lathing (in older properties) due to movement, vibration or ageing.
	3 A skim coat has suffered loss of adhesion to plasterboard, due either to the plasterboard being the wrong way round, or the wrong plaster being applied.

Remedies	1 Remove all plaster from affected area, and clean off loose material; replaster using bonding-type base coat. If necessary roughen the concrete surface and/or use a bonding agent.
	2 Remove all loose plaster, clean up laths and replaster. If deterioration is extensive it may be preferable to replace the old lath and plaster work entirely with new construction, for example using plasterboard.
	3 Remove all plaster from affected area, and clean up boards; replaster using appropriate materials, together with a bonding agent if necessary.

Cross references	Part I page no	Part II other defect sheet references		Part III slide no
	26 27	D1 D2 D3	D5 D6 D8	25

Defect	TOP COAT OF PLASTER LOOSE
Location	Walls and ceilings
Symptoms	The top coat of plaster has come away from the base coat, so that it sounds hollow if tapped; cracking and bulging is probably evident. It may have come away altogether exposing the undercoat plaster.
Checks/ questions	* What is the background structure ? * Is the undercoat adhering firmly to the back-ground ? * What type of base and finish coats appear to have been used ? * What is the extent of hollowness ?
Action	Refer to surveyor.

Defect	TOP COAT OF PLASTER LOOSE	D5

Location	Walls and ceilings

Causes	1 The background has shrunk after being plastered. (This can happen if the background is a cement-based material, such as in-situ concrete or breeze blocks, not fully cured when plaster was applied.) If the undercoat was also cement-based, it would shrink with the background, possibly splitting off the finish coat. 2 A strong expanding top coat has been applied to a weak or shrinkable undercoat.

Remedies	Remove all of the top coat from the affected area, and replaster using an appropriate material. If the undercoat is unsound it too must be renewed.

	Part I page no	Part II other defect sheet references		Part III slide no
Cross references	26 27	D1 D2 D3	D4 D6 D8	26

Defect	PITTING OF PLASTERWORK
Location	Internal wall finishes
Symptoms	Small conical shaped craters occur in the surface of the plaster generally with a small piece of foreign material in the base. Initially, loose pieces of plaster may be found.
Checks/ questions	* Is there any sign of foreign material in the base of the crater? * If so, is it obvious what it is?
Action	Instruct repair.

Defect	PITTING OF PLASTERWORK	D6
Location	Internal wall finishes	

Causes	The small piece of foreign material expands by absorbing water from either the air or the background wall.
	Impurities in the sand, plaster, cement and even clay bricks may also be the source of defect.
	Wetting of plastered surfaces can accelerate this type of pitting.

Remedies	Remove foreign material from craters and make good with appropriate filling material.

Cross references	Part I page no	Part II other defect sheet references	Part III slide no
	26	D4	27
	27	D5	
		D8	

Defect	DISCOLOURED AND BLISTERED DECORATION
Location	Internal wall finishes
Symptoms	<u>Discolouration</u> may be localised or general. It is usually permanent but may be temporary where dampness is present. Some discolouration is distinctly brown, pink, purple or black. It is particularly important when decorations are discoloured around air bricks. <u>Blistering</u> is usually localised and occurs on paint films or wallpapers. The blisters are quite often temporary and when broken may create sticky yellowish runs.
Checks/ questions	* Is the wall temporarily or permanently damp ? * What changes in colour have occurred and are they temporary or permanent ? * Are blisters present ? * To what use is the room put and what atmospheric conditions prevail ? * Is there discolouration near air bricks or ventilators ? * Are old flues lined or unlined ? * Are any lined flues sealed to appliances with bottom sealing plates ?
Action	Refer to surveyor.

Defect	DISCOLOURED AND BLISTERED DECORATION	D7
Location	Internal wall finishes	

Causes	1 Discolouration and blistering result from the presence of moisture. The colour changes are caused by chemical reaction, or mould growth which creates the characteristic pink, purple, brown and blackish discolouration. 2 Lack of properly fitted bottom sealing plate between a flue liner and a heating appliance or a generally deteriorated flue can allow fumes to find their way into rooms, causing discoloured decorations and danger to occupants.
Remedies	1 Remedy dampness (penetrating, condensation, rising damp). Redecorate after allowing the wall to dry out thoroughly. Note that surfaces with mould growth may need fungicide treatment. Ascertain the use of the room bearing in mind the toxic nature of such treatments. 2 Where necessary old flues can be lined or bottom ceiling plates can be fitted to flue liners.

Cross references	Part I page no	Part II other defect sheet references				Part III slide no
	27	H1	H4	H7	J4	28
		H2	H5	J1		
		H3	H6	J2		

Defect	TILES LOOSE OR FALLING OFF
Location	Internal wall finishes
Symptoms	Some **tiles** sound hollow when tapped and may fall off. Hollowness usually occurs within the first year or so after fixing but falling off may occur later.
Checks/ questions	* Look at the backs of the tiles to see if they have come away cleanly without the adhesive, or whether tile and adhesive have come away from the background. * Check whether it seems as if enough adhesive was used. * Check whether the background has cracks (due to shrinkage).
Action	Instruct repair.

Defect	TILES LOOSE OR FALLING OFF	D8
Location	Internal wall finishes	

Causes	1 Poor workmanship; too little area covered with adhesive.
	2 Shrinkage of background causes tiles to be forced loose (concrete walls, white calcium silicate bricks and woodwool slabs are vulnerable).
	3 Expansion of tiles, if fresh from the kiln when fixed.
	4 Use of non-waterproof adhesive in wet areas (eg shower cubicles, around sinks, baths and basins).

Remedies	For all four causes, refix the tiles after cleaning them, using a flexible adhesive to allow for future movement. Use waterproof adhesive in wet areas.

Cross references	Part I page no	Part II other defect sheet references					Part III slide no
	27	D1	D4	H1	H4	H7	29
		D2	D5	H2	H5		
		D3	D6	H3	H6		

Defect	PEELING FINISHES ON JOINERY
Location	Internal cupboards and shelves
Symptoms	Plastic, melamine, formica surfaces to kitchen fitments and other cupboards start to peel off the timber base.
Checks/ questions	* Is the material under the surface finish (probably chipboard, blockboard or plywood) damp ?
Action	Instruct repair.

Defect	PEELING FINISHES ON JOINERY	D9
Location	Internal cupboards and shelves	
Causes	Dampness causes disintegration of some timber products, break-down of adhesive and loss of strength.	
Remedies	Rectify cause of dampness, replace defective timber boards or sheets, refix surface material.	

Cross references	Part I page no	Part II other defect sheet references	Part III slide no
	30	H1 to H12	

Defect	FAULTY DOOR OPERATION
Location	Internal doors
Symptoms	Doors may stick and not open easily or close properly.
Checks/ questions	* Is the door or lock sticking ? * Has the door dropped on its hinges ? * Are the hinges loose ? * Is the door distorted ?
Action	Instruct repair.

Defect	FAULTY DOOR OPERATION	D10
Location	Internal doors	

Causes	1 Lock spring broken or worn out, or striking plate out of position. 2 Door has been hung on hinges which are too light or it has been removed to fit carpet and not properly rehung. 3 Hinge screws are loose or too small. 4 Door has swollen or warped.

Remedies	1 Replace lock, or refix striking plate. 2 Fit heavier hinges - possibly rising butts to clear carpets. 3 Tighten screws or fit bigger screws. 4 Plane or trim door to fit; or refix door stops.

Cross references	Part I page no	Part II other defect sheet references	Part III slide no
	30	C6	

Defect	PEELING AND FLAKING PAINTWORK
Location	Applied decoration
Symptoms	Paint peeling off in large sheets, or flaking off in smaller pieces, sometimes from new surfaces but more usually from old, redecorated surfaces.
Checks/ questions	* Is the exposed surface new or old work ? * Is there evidence of dampness or history of it ? * Are there signs of dirt or efflorescence on the back of paint that has come away ? * What is the condition of any previous decoration exposed ? * Is there evidence of dirt or grease on the exposed surface ?
Action	If no evidence of dampness, instruct redecoration, otherwise refer to surveyor.

Defect	PEELING AND FLAKING PAINTWORK	D11

Location	Applied decoration

Causes	1 <u>Previously decorated surfaces</u> The usual cause is poor preparation of the previous surface. For example, problems can arise if dirt or grease were not thoroughly cleaned off, deteriorated or loose paint films not removed, or if old gloss surfaces were not rubbed down. Modern decorating materials are not always compatible with previous decorations such as distemper. 2 <u>New surfaces</u> Efflorescence can occur under the paint film if it is applied before the background has dried out. 3 Dampness can cause this defect in both new and old work.
Remedies	1 Remove all decorations down to a firmly adhering, sound, clean surface, rub down any gloss paint surfaces and redecorate with suitable materials. 2 Clean off all loose paint and effloresence, ensure the surface is thoroughly dry and redecorate. 3 Remedy cause of dampness, allow surface to dry out and redecorate.

Cross references	Part I page no	Part II other defect sheet references	Part III slide no
	28	D3	37

FLOORS

The figures in the boxes on the opposite page are the reference numbers of the defect sheets which explain how to deal with the defects.

Questions to ask which will lead you to the correct defect sheet:

WHAT IS THE DEFECT ?

IS IT ASSOCIATED WITH A TIMBER FLOOR STRUCTURE ?

IS IT ASSOCIATED WITH A CONCRETE FLOOR SLAB OR SCREED ?

IS IT IN THE FLOOR FINISH ?

E

	WHERE IS THE DEFECT?		E
WHAT IS THE DEFECT?	Timber floor	Concrete floor or screed	Floor finish
Collapse	E1		
Warping and shrinking	E2		
Disintegration			E5
Lifting, curling and cracking		E3 E4	E6 E8 E7
Loss of adhesion		E3	E9

Defect	COLLAPSED SUSPENDED TIMBER FLOOR
Location	Floor
Symptoms	The floor may collapse generally or locally. Localised failure is usually in the region of doors in external walls. Whilst floor boards themselves may fail, damage is more likely to be confined to joists and supporting wall-plates.
Checks/ questions	* Where is the collapse? * Are there any signs of fungal growth? * Are there any signs of woodworm? * Is the rot confined to the end of joists? * Is there any evidence of dampness in the region of attack? * Is the floor excessively loaded or apparently not built strongly enough for the load at any point?
Action	Refer to surveyor.

Defect	COLLAPSED SUSPENDED TIMBER FLOOR	E1
Location	Floor	

Causes

1 <u>Fungal attack</u> due to damp conditions under the floor. If the attack is localised and confined to the end of joists it is likely that it has been caused by wet rot. More general attack is likely to be due to dry rot.

2 <u>Woodworm</u> can attack floorboards and joists.

3 <u>Excessive floor loading</u>.

4 <u>Ground movement</u> causes the brickwork supporting the floor joists to drop.

Remedies

1 Locate and eradicate the source of dampness. Remove affected and adjoining timber and replace with treated timber.

2 Treat the insect attack in the appropriate manner.

3 Strengthen or replace floor to carry loadings. Excessive loadings should be avoided.

4 The reasons for ground movement should be ascertained and steps taken to prevent further subsidence.

Cross references	Part I page no	Part II other defect sheet references		Part III slide no
	28	A1 K2 E2 K3 K1		30

Defect	WARPING AND SHRINKING FLOORBOARDS
Location	Floors
Symptoms	Gaps appear between timber boards and edges curl upwards. Covering laid on the boards may become ridged along the board joints and the ridges may crack.
Checks/ questions	* Are the boards tongued and grooved? * Does the air in the building ever become very dry?
Action	Refer to surveyor.

Defect	WARPING AND SHRINKING FLOORBOARDS	E2
Location	Floors	
Causes	Deformation is usually because the boards have not dried out adequately before being fixed. Shrinkage occurs which the nails are not able to hold. This leads to gaps and then curling, particularly where the boards are not tongued and grooved. As the boards deform, any covering on top of the boards is also deformed.	
Remedies	Nail down loose boards and check existing nailing. The boards can then be planed or sanded to an overall flat surface.	

	Part I page no	Part II other defect sheet references	Part III slide no
Cross references	28	E1	31

Defect	LIFTING, CURLING AND CRACKING OF CONCRETE SCREEDS
Location	Floors
Symptoms	First indications of defective floor screeds are cracks, splits or unevenness of the floor finishing laid on top of the screed. Where the floor is tiled, the faults may occur along clear lines.
Checks/ questions	* What is the extent of cracking, splitting or unevenness of floor finishing? * Remove part of the floor finishing, if loose, and examine the state of the screed. * To what extent is it cracked, broken up or hollow sounding when tapped? * Does the underlying concrete floor slab appear sound?
Action	Refer to surveyor.

Defect	LIFTING, CURLING AND CRACKING OF CONCRETE SCREEDS	E3

Location	Floors

Causes	1 Incorrect mix of screed or inadequate curing time or laid in too large bays. 2 Disturbance of base concrete.

Remedies	The remedial action will obviously depend on the state of the screed and may involve cutting out and patching, levelling off areas or total renewal of screed in severe cases.

Cross references	Part I page no	Part II other defect sheet references	Part III slide no
	28	E4 E7	32

Defect	LIFTING AND CRACKING OF CONCRETE FLOORS
Location	Ground floor
Symptoms	Initial indications are doors binding (scraping) on the floor. As the defect worsens, lifting and arching become more pronounced and the surface of the concrete cracks. Some outward movement of perimeter walls in the region of the damp-proof course and some extrusion (squeezing) of damp-proof course material may occur.
Checks/ questions	* What is the extent of lifting, arching and cracking of concrete? * Do the perimeter walls appear to have moved outwards in the region of the damp-proof course? * Is there any extrusion of the damp-proof course material?
Action	Refer to surveyor.

Defect	LIFTING AND CRACKING OF CONCRETE FLOORS	E4
Location	Ground floor	
Causes	Chemical attack or unstable aggregates in the concrete cause it to expand.	
Remedies	Remove the concrete floor and hard core and replace with materials not susceptible to chemical attack. Where the lifting of the concrete is not excessive it may be possible to cut around the perimeter and convert the gap into a compressible joint capable of dealing with future expansion.	

Cross reference	Part I page no	Part II other defect sheet references	Part III slide no
	28	E3 E7	33

Defect	SWEATING AND DISINTEGRATION OF MAG-NESITE (COMPOSITION) FLOOR SURFACES
Location	Floors
Symptoms	Magnesite floor surfaces sometimes disintegrate, gradually at first, becoming worse if allowed to continue. This type of flooring may also be seen to sweat during damp weather conditions.
Checks/ questions	* Is the building known to have a damp-proof membrane? * Are the floors adequately maintained, ie polished regularly? * Does the floor 'sweat'? * What ventilation is provided?
Action	Refer to surveyor.

Defect	SWEATING AND DISINTEGRATION OF MAG-NESITE (COMPOSITION) FLOOR SURFACES	E5
Location	Floors	
Causes	Magnesite floor finish can absorb moisture from the air; the surface then appears to sweat. Cleaning water applied to a badly maintained floor may penetrate, leading to disintegration. Where there is no damp-proof membrane (or a defective one) beneath the flooring, rising damp may affect the flooring from below.	
Remedies	Apply polish if the floor appears to sweat and there are no signs of disintegration. Adequate ventilation must be provided. Renew severely disintegrated flooring if rising damp is likely to continue. Remedy defective or absent damp-proof membrane.	

Cross references	Part I page no	Part II other defect sheet references	Part III slide no
	28	H1 H11 H12	

Defect	LIFTING OF WOOD BLOCKS
Location	Floors
Symptoms	Wood blocks lift upwards over large areas or along two or three rows only.
Checks/ questions	* Have the blocks come away from the adhesive or have the blocks and adhesive come away from the floor screed? * Is there any sign of dampness? * Is there any sign of fungal attack?
Action	Refer to surveyor.

Defect	LIFTING OF WOOD BLOCKS	E6

Location	Floors

Causes	The usual cause is an increase in moisture content of the blocks, causing them to swell. Blocks are forced up from their bedding. This can arise when blocks are laid in a very dry condition in a building where the humidity is subsequently high.

Remedies	Dry out the blocks and relay them after the source of dampness is eradicated. Where humidity conditions are high, the blocks should be 'conditioned' to a higher humidity content before relaying. The provision of a compression joint at the perimeter is highly recommended.

Cross references	Part I page no	Part II other defect sheet references	Part III slide no
	28	H1 H11 H12	34

Defect	LIFTING OF CLAY TILES
Location	Floors
Symptoms	Clay floor tiles can lift either over a large area or along two or three rows and break away from the bedding. Indications of lifting can sometimes be detected by tapping – they sound hollow.
Checks/ questions	* Do the tiles sound hollow when tapped ? * Are the tiles arched or uneven in any way ? * Have cracking sounds been heard from the tiles by tenants ?
Action	Refer to surveyor.

Defect	LIFTING OF CLAY TILES	E7
Location	Floors	

Causes	1 <u>Irreversible expansion</u> caused by moisture from the air, cleaning operations or during construction.
	2 <u>Thermal movement</u> may break the bond. Differential shrinkage can occur between tile and screed.
	3 <u>Shrinkage of the floor screed</u> sometimes occurs within a year of tiles being laid.

Remedies	Where large areas are defective, take up all the tiles and relay them.
	The provision of a movement joint is strongly recommended.

Cross references	Part I page no	Part II other defect sheet references	Part III slide no
	28	E3 E4	35

Defect	LIFTING AND DETERIORATION OF PLASTIC FLOOR TILES
Location	Floors
Symptoms	Tiles are loose or their edges have lifted. The tile edges may show a white saltlike substance or, in extreme cases, disintegrate. This defect may apply to individual tiles or large areas of the floor. The tiles may be thermoplastic or pvc.
Checks/ questions	* Is the defect confined to a few tiles or to large areas of the floor? * Is there known to be a damp-proof membrane beneath the floor? * How long ago was the building completed?
Action	Refer to surveyor.

Defect	LIFTING AND DETERIORATION OF PLASTIC FLOOR TILES	E8

Location	Floors

Causes	Water passes through the concrete base on which the tiles are laid, due to the absence of a damp proof membrane or the presence of excess construction water. Alternatively, excessive water may have been used for cleaning purposes. Less frequently, tiles have not been stuck down properly.

Remedies	Check the source of water. Remedy the absence of a damp-proof membrane by laying asphalt, retile. Avoid excessive swillage during cleaning. Where it is difficult to keep the concrete dry, a finish which is less vulnerable to water should be used.

Cross references	Part I page no	Part II other defect sheet references	Part III slide no
	28	H1 H11 H12	36

Defect	LOSS OF ADHESION OF SHEET FLOORING
Location	Floors
Symptoms	Blisters appear in the sheeting and large areas may have come away from the screed and/or rippled.
Checks/ questions	* What is the extent of blistering or rippling? * Lift part of the sheeting, and see if the adhesive is tacky, dry or brittle. * Is there any pronounced smell associated with the adhesive? * Is there any evidence of dampness? * Is a damp-proof membrane known to exist? * How is the floor cleaned? * Is the floor excessively loaded?
Action	Refer to surveyor.

Defect	LOSS OF ADHESION OF SHEET FLOORING	E9
Location	Floors	

Causes	1 Moisture causes dimensional changes to this type of sheeting (eg rippling). The most likely reason is rising damp. 2 An unsuitable adhesive has been used, or the solvent contained in the adhesive sometimes becomes trapped leading to eventual loss of adhesion. A pronounced smell is usually associated with the presence of trapped solvent.

Remedies	1 Check the reason for dampness and where necessary incorporate a surface damp-proof membrane. Replace the finish with material less susceptible to water. 2 Replace the sheeting using a suitable (recommended) adhesive.

Cross references	Part I page no	Part II other defect sheet references	Part III slide no
	28	H1 H11 H12	

PLUMBING, HEATING AND DRAINS

The figures in the boxes on the opposite page are the reference numbers of the defect sheets which explain how to deal with the defects.

Questions to ask which will lead you to the correct defect sheet:

WHAT IS THE DEFECT?

IS IT ASSOCIATED WITH COLD WATER TANKS AND SYSTEMS?

IS IT ASSOCIATED WITH THE HOT WATER AND/OR HEATING SYSTEM?

IS IT A PIPEWORK DEFECT?

IS IT ASSOCIATED WITH TRAPS UNDER APPLIANCES OR WITH WASTE PIPES?

IS IT ASSOCIATED WITH DRAINS?

F

WHAT IS THE DEFECT?	WHERE IS THE DEFECT?			F
	Cold water system	Hot water system	Heating system	Wastes, traps and drains
Leaking	F1 F2	F2		
Furring up, dripping and overflowing	F5	F4		
Tank not filling properly	F5			
Knocking (hammer), noisiness and vibration	F6	F6		
Distortion and softening of pipes				F7
Blockage in pipe				F8
Frozen pipes	F3	F3		F3
Blocked drain				F9
Boiler not working		F10	F10	
Heating not working			F11 F12	

PLUMBING, HEATING AND DRAINS

Defect	LEAKS IN GALVANISED COLD WATER TANKS
Location	Plumbing systems
Symptoms	Water is seen leaking from the bottom or the sides of galvanised cold water tanks. Inside, there are invariably signs of rust in the region of the leak and often elsewhere.
Checks/ questions	* Is the ceiling damp in the vicinity of the tank ? * Is the point of leakage obvious ? * Is the rust on the inside of the tank extensive or limited to areas of joints etc ? * Have any metal objects been dropped into the tank and caused localised corrosion ?
Action	Instruct repair for minor leak, otherwise refer to surveyor.

Defect	LEAKS IN GALVANISED COLD WATER TANKS	F1
Location	Plumbing systems	

Causes	1 Chemical action on the galvanised coating of the tank leaves the tank unprotected against rusting.
	2 Foreign metal bodies have been accidentally dropped in and caused localised corrosion.
	3 Bi-metallic corrosion occurs where dissimilar metals have been used in fittings connected to the tank.

Remedies	Treatment depends on the extent of the corrosion. Patch single leaks and coat the whole of the inside with a non-tainting bitumen paint. Consideration should be given to rusting spots which are not actually leaking. It may be preferable to replace the tank with a plastic one.

Cross references	Part I page no	Part II other defect sheet references	Part III slide no
	36	H10 H12 K4	

Defect	LEAKS AT JOINTS
Location	Plumbing systems
Symptoms	Leaks vary from slight weeping (difficult to see) to major leaks which are self-evident. If the pipes are iron or steel there may be signs of rusting on the painted surface.
Checks/ questions	* What is the extent of the leak ? * How long has the joint been leaking ? * What type of joint is it ? * Does the leak occur frequently ?
Action	Refer to surveyor.

Defect	LEAKS AT JOINTS	F2
Location	Plumbing systems	

Causes	1 Thermal expansion is the most common cause. Pipes frequently alter length as a result of expansion and if the pipe is rigidly fixed it fails at the weakest point, usually a joint.
	2 Thermal contraction is usually responsible for the pulling out of compression joints.
	3 The joint was badly made in the first place.
	4 Bi-metallic corrosion: the joint is made up of two incompatible metals.
	5 Chemical action of the fluxes used to make the joint.

Remedies	1 Remove the constraint to enable expansion to develop fully. This may involve changing the position of a pipe run or clearing an obstruction. Alternatively, special expansion fittings might be utilised.
	2 Remake compression joint.
	3 Tighten or remake joint.
	4 Renew joint, selecting materials so that bi-metallic corrosion no longer occurs.
	5 Replace joint ensuring that any harmful material is removed.

	Part I page no	Part II other defect sheet references		Part III slide no
Cross references	39	F3 F7 H5	H10	40

Defect	FROZEN PIPES
Location	Plumbing systems
Symptoms	During very cold weather the supply of water to taps, tanks, cisterns, basins, sinks or baths may freeze. Following a thaw, pipes may fracture and joints become defective, with obvious leakage.
Checks/ questions	* Check procedures are usually part of the remedial action. Whilst the pipes are frozen, the main difficulty will be in locating the blockage before attempting to thaw it out. Unlagged and particularly exposed pipework are obvious starting points. Where the pipe has burst or a joint become defective, this is obvious and the supply must be turned off as soon as possible, to avoid damage by water.
Action	Instruct repair; inform surveyor.

Defect	FROZEN PIPES	F3
Location	Plumbing systems	

Causes	Whenever the temperature drops below freezing point, water in pipes may freeze, cutting off the flow. This may be because the building is generally unheated or because particular pipes are unlagged or exposed. Following a thaw, pipes may be fractured because water expands on freezing, or joints may become defective. When sinks, basins or baths fail to empty, this is because water in waste pipes has frozen.

| Remedies | Try thawing out from the delivery end first, using cloths soaked in hot water or a gradual rising of temperature around the pipe using electrical appliances. Intensive heating using blow torches should only be attempted by a plumber. Frozen waste pipes can be dealt with by repeatedly pouring hot water over the frozen outlet.

Repairs to burst pipes and defective joints should be carried out by a plumber. To avoid future trouble, resiting and/or lagging of pipes should be considered by the surveyor. |
|---|---|

Cross references	Part I page no	Part II other defect sheet references	Part III slide no
	39	F2	41

119

Defect	FURRING OF PIPES
Location	Hot water system
Symptoms	Over a period of time the amount of hot water available diminishes and eventually may become nothing more than a trickle.
Checks/ questions	* Has the amount of water available noticeably lessened over a period of time ? * Is the area a known hard water area ? * Is there a history of similar symptoms in houses in the area ?
Action	Refer to surveyor.

Defect	FURRING OF PIPES	F4
Location	Hot water system	

Causes	The most likely reason for this defect is the gradual furring up of pipes from the boiler to the hot water system especially in direct systems. In hard water areas, chalk scale is deposited in the pipes and the bore is gradually reduced. The rate of furring up increases if the boiler is run at a high temperature.

Remedies	If the trouble is recognised before it becomes too serious, a scale removing treatment can be used. Firms specialising in this technique exist in most areas.
	Where the defect has gone too far, replace the furred-up lengths of pipe.
	The use of water softening equipment or the fitting of a thermostat to keep the hot water below 60°C should also be considered.

Cross references	Part I page no	Part II other defect sheet references	Part III slide no
	40		42

Defect	MALFUNCTIONING BALL VALVES
Location	Plumbing systems
Symptoms	Water drips or flows out of the overflow pipe of tanks and cisterns. Sometimes the tank or cistern will fail to fill.
Checks/ questions	* Is water flowing or dripping from the overflow pipe? * Is the float metal or plastic? * If metal, is the float corroded? * Is there any evidence of water in the float? (If necessary turn off the water, remove float and shake.) * Are there any obvious splits or holes which might have allowed water to enter the float? * Is the valve closing properly when the cistern or tank is full, or does water continue to flow? * Is the valve stuck in the fully closed position allowing no water to enter?
Action	Instruct repair.

Defect	MALFUNCTIONING BALL VALVES	F5

Location	Plumbing systems

Causes

The commonest faults are:

1 The valve washer may have split or worn and is no longer seated properly, so allowing water to continue to flow. Alternatively, the seating may have worn.

2 The valve plunger may stick due to grit or scale. This may either slow down or prevent filling, or prevent the valve fully cutting off the flow when the tank or cistern is full.

3 The float may have been punctured or corroded and partially filled with water. When this happens the valve stays partly open.

Remedies

1 Replace washer and/or nozzle seating preferably with nylon parts.

2 Remove grit by allowing a full flow of water to flush out the system and remove any deposit.

3 Replace damaged float with a plastic one.

Cross references	Part I page no	Part II other defect sheet references	Part III slide no
	36	F6￼H5￼K4	

Defect	WATER HAMMER/KNOCKING PIPES
Location	Plumbing systems
Symptoms	When a tap or valve is opened or closed a distinctive and intermittent hammering or thumping sound is heard. There may also be vibration in the pipework.
Checks/ questions	* Which tap or valve causes water hammer? Turn each tap and valve on and off to ascertain this. * What is the state of the washer on an offending tap? * Are any pipes of significantly different diameter to the rest of the system? * Do any lengths of pipe seem to be inadequately supported?
Action	Instruct repair.

Defect	WATER HAMMER/KNOCKING PIPES	F6

Location	Plumbing systems

Causes	The primary cause is sudden increase in pressure in the system causing vibration in the mechanism of a tap, valve or stop cock connected to the rising main, or in a length of pipe inadequately supported. This increase in pressure may be due to: 1 A loose or defective washer 2 A wrongly sized ball valve 3 Sections of pipework of significantly different diameter 4 Opening the main stop cock too far.

Remedies	1 Replace washer. 2 Increase size of float of ball valve. 3 Replace pipework of different diameter if the noise is a nuisance. 4 Reduce pressure by adjusting stop cock. 5 Fix pipes if inadequately supported. Note Regular maintenance of tap washers is an obvious precaution against this defect.

Cross references	Part I page no	Part II other defect sheet references	Part III slide no
	40	F4 F5	

Defect	SOFTENING AND DISTORTION OF PLASTIC WASTE PIPES AND TRAPS
Location	Plumbing systems
Symptoms	Waste pipes or traps may be bowed or distorted and water may not flow away properly. There may also be some leakage.
Checks/ questions	* How frequently is hot water poured down the waste pipe etc? * Is there any evidence of chemical cleaners, solvents or paint strippers having been recently poured away? * Is there any apparent leakage?
Action	Instruct repair.

Defect	SOFTENING AND DISTORTION OF PLASTIC WASTE PIPES AND TRAPS	F7
Location	Plumbing systems	
Causes	Hot water may gradually soften plastics after which distortion more easily occurs. The usual cause of this defect is misuse of the waste system. Chemical cleaners, solvents and paint strippers used in redecorating may have been poured away and attacked the inside of the trap. Such chemicals left for long periods in the trap may cause perforation and consequent leakage.	
Remedies	Replace defective wastes and traps. Where a particular plastic has not proved adequate in dealing with persistent hot water waste, use an alternative type. It is essential to warn tenants against misuse of appliances particularly with respect to chemical cleaners, solvents and stripping agents.	

Cross references	Part I page no	Part II other defect sheet references	Part III slide no
	39	F2 F8	

Defect	BLOCKED WASTE PIPES
Location	Plumbing systems
Symptoms	Water does not run away to waste; this is most frequently associated with kitchen sinks.
Checks/ questions	* Has the tenant already tried to clear the blockage? If so, how? * Is anything known to have been poured down which could cause blockage? (eg hot fat, tea leaves) * Are there any cleaning eyes available? * Are there signs of corrosion on the pipes or fittings? * Is it known what is causing the blockage? * Check waste pipe for back fall.
Action	Instruct clearance. For cause 2, refer to surveyor.

Defect	BLOCKED WASTE PIPES	F8
Location	Plumbing systems	

Causes	1 Household material that has become compacted or solidified. 2 Internal corrosion causing restricted flow and hence blockage by normal household waste. 3 Back fall in waste pipe.

Remedies	1 Clear by rodding or flushing with caustic soda (safety precautions necessary) or by drain clearing specialist in cases of persistent blockage. 2 Replace corroded section with more suitable material. 3 Relay waste pipe to proper fall.

Cross references	Part I page no	Part II other defect sheet references	Part III slide no
	33 34	F7 F9	43

Defect	BLOCKED DRAINS
Location	External works
Symptoms	Leakage may be seen from an inspection chamber or manhole and in some cases the cover may have lifted. In extreme cases a particular appliance may not empty and leaks may be seen in joints and pipes leading to the underground system.
Checks/ questions	* Beyond confirming the existence of a blocked drain, further checks are part of the remedial action.
Action	Arrange for clearance; inform surveyor if other than cause 1.

Defect	BLOCKED DRAINS	F9
Location	External works	

Causes	1 Drains become blocked as a result of deliberate or accidental misuse of sanitary appliances.
	2 Tree roots penetrate the joints or grow through pipes.
	3 Fungal growths gradually restrict flow through the pipe.
	4 If the pipe is flexible it may become excessively compressed.
	5 Rigid pipes may break.

Remedies	1 Attempt clearance using normal cleansing equipment and expertise.
	2 Remove root, or perhaps the entire tree or shrub. This may involve excavation both to remove and repair fractured or disjointed pipes.
	3 Identify fungal growth so that its food source can be identified and removed.
	4 Provided the deformation is temporary, releasing the blockage should return the pipe to its original shape.
	5 Ascertain the reason for breakage and replace broken pipes.

Cross references	Part I page no	Part II other defect sheet references	Part III slide no
	51	F8	

Defect	BOILER OR WATER HEATER NOT WORKING PROPERLY
Location	Appliance
Symptoms	Hot water supply or radiator system does not reach required temperature. Appliance may not work at all. Appliance may be difficult to ignite and start with loud noise (woomph!). Appliance may be smelly in operation.
Checks/ questions	* Is the boiler gas or oil fired? * Is there a service contract for the appliance? * Has pilot light gone out? * Is the gas supply turned off or the oil tank empty? * Is the air supply or ventilator to the room blocked? * When was the appliance last serviced? * Is the boiler controlled by a programmer/timer? * Is the failure sudden or has the problem gradually got worse? * Is the flame yellow or blue? * Is the boiler thermostat set properly? * Is the electrical supply to the controls switched on?
Action	Make checks; inform surveyor and refer to installation or service contractor if necessary.

Defect	BOILER OR WATER HEATER NOT WORKING PROPERLY	F10
Location	Appliance	

Causes	1 Fuel supply to the appliance may have been turned off or run out.
	2 Air supply or flue may have been blocked.
	3 Pilot light may have gone out.
	4 Water supply to the system may have failed and the boiler has failed safe.
	5 Gas supply pressure may need adjustment.
	6 Fuel supply of oil may be blocked.
	7 Burner component may need servicing.
	8 Ignition system may need servicing.
	9 Boiler thermostat may need servicing.
	10 Programmer/timer may need resetting or servicing.
	11 Electrical supply to controls may have failed or have been switched off.

Remedies	1 Check fuel supply and rectify.
	2 Make sure that air bricks, ventilators and flues are unobstructed.
	3 Re-light pilot light.
	4 Ensure that water supply is turned on and that system is not leaking.
	5 6 7 8 } Clean, adjust or replace components as necessary (service contractor).
	9 10 } Check setting, adjust if necessary. If still not working, refer to service contractor.
	11 Restore electrical supply.

Cross references	Part I page no	Part II other defect sheet references	Part III slide no
	37 38	F11 G2	

133

Defect	RADIATORS NOT WORKING PROPERLY
Location	In any room
Symptoms	Some or all radiators may not reach the required temperature.
Checks/ questions	Turn room thermostat up until it clicks, turn programmer/timer to 'heating constant', then test as follows: * Is boiler working? (Watch burner through perspex panel.) * Is boiler thermostat correctly set? * Is circulatory pump working? (Locate pump near boiler, switch off and on, listen for humming sound of pump working.) * Is room thermostat working? (Adjust required temperature up and down past actual temperature and check that pump starts and stops.) * Are all radiators too cold? * Are only some radiators or upper halves of radiators cold? * Are radiator valves turned on? * Is programmer/timer working? (Adjust, set heating to 'timed', revolve timer and listen for pump stopping and starting.) * Check that electrical supply to boiler, pump and controls is fitted with fuse and switched on. * Does the water in the radiator system contain a corrosion inhibitor?
Action	Make checks; inform surveyor and refer to service contractor if necessary.

Defects	RADIATORS NOT WORKING PROPERLY	F11
Location	In any room	

Causes	1 Boiler not working – see F10.
	2 Boiler thermostat needs adjusting/servicing.
	3 Room thermostat needs adjusting/servicing.
	4 Programmer/timer needs adjusting/servicing.
	5 Circulatory pump needs servicing.
	6 Radiator system contains air pockets; radiators or pipes may be damaged and leak or suck in air.
	7 Radiators turned off or system needs balancing.
	8 Radiators sludged or furred up with scale.
	9 Thermostatically controlled radiator valves may be defective.
	10 Electrical supply to controls may have fused.
	11 Internal corrosion may be taking place, giving rise to hydrogen gas, which accumulates in radiators, and a black sludge which may block the pump.

Remedies	Carry out all checks to isolate problems. Adjust all controls to appropriate settings. Test system. If still not working properly instruct service contractor to test, service, adjust or repair as necessary.
	If cause 6 (air locks), then bleed air from radiator system by opening air bleed valves at top of end of radiator with bleed key and then close valves (contractor or surveyor).
	If cause 11, drain system, flush out and re-fill including a corrosion inhibitor (contractor or surveyor).

Cross references	Part I page no	Part II other defect sheet references	Part III slide no
	41 42	F10 G2	

Defect	WARM AIR HEATING NOT WORKING PROPERLY
Location	General or in a specific room
Symptoms	Inadequate heating in some or all rooms.
Checks/ questions	Turn room thermostat up until it clicks, turn programmer/timer to 'heating constant' then test as follows: * Is heat exchanger working? (Locate and watch burner.) * Is fan working? (Locate and listen.) * Is air filter blocked? (Locate and check.) * Are intake or outlet grilles obstructed? * Is room thermostat working? (Adjust required temperature up and down past actual temperature and check that fan starts after short interval then stops.) * Is programmer/timer working? (Adjust, set heating to 'timed', revolve timer and listen for fan starting and stopping.)
Action	Make checks; inform surveyor and refer to service contractor if necessary.

Defect	WARM AIR HEATING NOT WORKING PROPERLY	F12
Location	General or in a specific room	

Causes	1 Heat exchanger may not be working.
	2 Room thermostat may need adjusting or servicing.
	3 Programmer/timer may need adjusting or servicing.
	4 Fan may need servicing.
	5 Intake or outlet grilles may be obstructed.
	6 Electrical supply to controls etc may have fused or be switched off.
	7 Gas supply may be turned off.
	8 Pilot light may have gone out.

Remedies	Carry out all checks to isolate problem. Adjust controls to appropriate settings. Make sure that all grilles are unobstructed. Light pilot. Check that electrical supply to heat exchanger, fan and controls is fitted with appropriate fuse and switched on. Test system. If still not working properly, instruct service contractor to test, service, adjust or repair as necessary.

Cross references	Part I page no	Part II other defect sheet references	Part III slide no
	42	G2	

ELECTRICITY SUPPLY AND DISTRIBUTION

The figures in the boxes on the opposite page are the reference numbers of the defect sheets which explain how to deal with the defects.

Questions to ask which will lead you to the correct defect sheet:

WHAT IS THE DEFECT?

DOES IT CAUSE FUSES TO BLOW
(REPEATEDLY) OR CIRCUIT BREAKERS
TO OPERATE?

IS IT IN AN ELECTRICAL APPLIANCE OR
FLEX TO THE APPLIANCE?

IS THERE AN OBVIOUS DEFECT IN THE CIRCUIT
WIRING?

G

WHAT IS THE DEFECT ?	WHERE IS THE DEFECT ?		G
	Fuse box	Fitment or flex to appliance	Circuit wiring
Blown fuses	G1	G2	
Overheating		G1	G1
Brittle insulation			G1

Defect	FAILURE OF ELECTRICAL INSULATION
Location	Electricity supply and distribution
Symptoms	Fuses blow or circuit breakers operate cutting off the supply to the whole system (or sub-system). Flexible cable overheats and insulation becomes brittle.
Checks/ questions	* What is the condition of light flexes and leads from appliances to power points etc? * What is the obvious condition of main circuit wiring. Is it pvc coated or does it run in metal conduit? * How old is the circuit wiring? * Is the tenant obviously overloading power points or light sockets? Note Beyond the above checks, all circuit testing should be carried out by a qualified electrician.
Action	Refer to electrician; inform surveyor.

Defect	FAILURE OF ELECTRICAL INSULATION	G1
Location	Electricity supply and distribution	
Causes	Flexible connections which have become brittle with age or exposed to heat and light may be moved or disturbed when re-decorating is carried out. Cleaning of light fittings, or even replacing bulbs, can have a similar effect, particularly on light flexes. Insufficient socket outlets can mean extensive use of two way adaptors and possible circuit overload.	
Remedies	Evidence of overloading and overheating is usually indicative of the whole system requiring renewal. Individual light flexes are susceptible to a more rapid rate of deterioration than circuit wiring and should be checked regularly. Instruct replacement of light flexes if in poor condition, but for any other failings instruct electrician to carry out inspection and test, particularly if property was not rewired on conversion.	

	Part I page no	Part II other defect sheet references	Part III slide no
Cross references	46	G2	

141

Defect	ELECTRICAL APPLIANCE NOT WORKING
Location	Anywhere indoors
Symptoms	The appliance fails to work when switched on.
Checks/ questions	* Is electrical supply on? * Is a wire loose at plug end or the appliance end of the flex? * Has the plug fuse blown? (if modern square pin plug is fitted). * Has a fuse blown at the fuse board? * Does the appliance emit smoke when switched on, or get hot? * If a light, check whether bulb has blown. Note It can be extremely dangerous to use household appliances in the garden and such use should be discouraged unless the appliance is specifically designed for use outside.
Action	Refer to an electrician or supplier unless cause 1 or 2 can be easily rectified.

Defect	ELECTRICAL APPLIANCE NOT WORKING	G2
Location	Anywhere indoors	
Causes	1 Loose wire. 2 Fuse has blown. 3 Faulty appliance. 4 Insulation breakdown.	
Remedies	1 Reconnect the wires. 2 Replace fuse (correct size) and try again. If still faulty refer to electrician. 3 Call in specialist or return to supplier. Do-it-yourself electrical repairs can be dangerous and cause fatal accidents. If you have the slightest doubt about doing even a simple job call on an electrician or other competent person.	

Cross references	Part I page no	Part II other defect sheet references	Part III slide no
	47 48	F10 G1 F11 F12	

DAMP

The figures in the boxes on the opposite page are the reference numbers of the defect sheets which explain how to deal with the defects.

Questions to ask which will lead you to the correct defect sheet:

WHAT SORT OF DAMP IS IT?

IS IT GENERAL OR PATCHY DAMP?

IF ON THE FLOOR, IS IT THE GROUND FLOOR?

IF ON A WALL, IS IT AN INTERNAL WALL OR A SOLID OR CAVITY EXTERNAL WALL?

IF ON A CEILING, IS IT IMMEDIATELY UNDER THE ROOF?

H

| WHERE IS IT DAMP? | WHAT SORT OF DAMP? | | | H |
	Associated with rain	Associated with cold and/or damp weather	Semi-permanent	Not permanent but not associated with rain or cold damp weather
Basement		H1	H1	
Ground floor			H11	H12
Floor generally				H12
Wall near ground level			H2	
Inside face of external solid wall	H3			
Inside face of external cavity wall	H4			
Generally on a wall		H6		H6
In patches on a wall				H5
Near a chimney breast	H7			H7
Ceiling generally	H9	H9		H10 H12
Ceiling/top of wall below roof	H8 H10 H9	H8 H9		

DAMP

Defect	DAMP IN BASEMENTS
Location	Basements
Symptoms	Damp is visible on walls and floors. In severe cases water may be leaking or seeping through walls or floors, or may be generally present.
Checks/ questions	* Is the point of water penetration obvious? If not wipe clean and then try to see where the water is entering. * Is the damp periodic and does it coincide with or follow rain? * Was the basement ever waterproofed? If so, how? * Is there any adjacent excavation of the subsoil? * What form of heating is used and how is it used?
Action	Refer to surveyor.

Defect	DAMP IN BASEMENTS	H1
Location	Basements	

Causes	1 Ground water under pressure penetrates construction joints.
	2 Damp penetration from subsoil through cracked basement walls.
	3 Condensation. This is likely to arise when heating is used intermittently and particularly when paraffin heaters, where water is one of the products of combustion, are used without adequate ventilation.

Remedies	1 Relieve ground water under pressure with additional land drains.
	2 Waterproof cracked walls.
	3 Relieve condensation by improving insulation (dry lining of internal walls for example), and possibly ventilation.

Cross references	Part I page no	Part II other defect sheet references			Part III slide no
	17	D7	E5	E9	
	45	D8	E6		
	55	D9	E8		

Defect	SEMI-PERMANENT DAMP
Location	Walls at or near ground level
Symptoms	Semi-permanent damp can be seen on wall surfaces from ground level up to approximately 750 mm (30 in) or even higher in severe cases. Decorations may be damp, blistered and discoloured or dried out and pushed off the wall by a salt deposit. There may be rot in floor and skirting boards adjacent to the defective wall.
Checks/ questions	* Does the building have an obvious damp-proof course? * Are the decorations damp, blistered or discoloured? * Is there any sign of wood rot in adjacent floor and skirting boards? * Does the damp vary with weather conditions?
Action	Refer to surveyor.

Defect	SEMI-PERMANENT DAMP	H2
Location	Walls at or near ground level	

Causes	This type of damp is due to one or more of the following: 1 Lack of a damp-proof course 2 By-passing of the damp-proof course 3 Failure of the damp-proof course

Remedies	1 Provide damp-proof course. 2 Remove soil or material bridging damp-proof course. 3 Repair or replace damp-proof course. Additional work such as renewal of plaster or skirting board will be required. Advise the tenant accordingly.

Cross references	Part I page no	Part II other defect sheet references	Part III slide no
	17 55	D7 D8 D9	44 45 46

Defect	DAMP SOLID WALL ASSOCIATED WITH RAIN
Location	Solid walls
Symptoms	Decorated internal surfaces of solid external walls subject to driving rain are visibly damp shortly after the rain. When the wall dries out stains can be seen and there might also be evidence of surface staining or mould growth under the surface.
Checks/ questions	* Does the damp appear after rain ? * Is the damp all over the wall area or is it patchy ? * If patchy, does it correspond to any external defect such as a defective downpipe, cracks in applied rendering or defective joints in brickwork (pointing) ? * Is there evidence of efflorescence or mould growth under the surface ? * Make sure the damp is not due to condensation, usually more prolonged than damp due to inter-mittent rain.
Action	Refer to surveyor.

Defect	AMP SOLID WALL ASSOCIATED WITH RAIN	H3
Location	Solid walls	

Causes	1 The wall cannot resist direct penetration of rain due to intensity of rain, deteriorating brickwork joints or rendering. 2 Defective guttering or downpipe.
Remedies	1 Render walls to resist rain penetration. Alternatively, materials such as ship-lap boarding should be considered. In less serious cases, apply water repellant. Repoint defective mortar joints. 2 Repair or replace defective guttering or down-pipes.

Cross references	Part I page no	Part II other defect sheet references		Part III slide no
	14 55	B6 B7 D7	D8 D9 J4	47

Defect	DAMP CAVITY WALL ASSOCIATED WITH RAIN
Location	Cavity walls
Symptoms	Damp occurs shortly after rain on the internal decorated surface at damp-proof course level, or above window and door openings or over the surface generally. There is no sign of damp during dry periods, although a damp wall may take time to dry out.
Checks/ questions	* Does the damp occur only after rain ? * How long does it take to dry out ? * Where is the damp most prominent ? * Is the cavity foam-filled ?
Action	Refer to surveyor.

Defect	DAMP CAVITY WALL ASSOCIATED WITH RAIN	H4

Location	Cavity walls

Causes	1 Excess mortar build up at various points in the cavity. 2 Wall ties put in wrongly – they slope down towards inner wall. 3 Cavity bridge formed by injected foam. 4 Damp-proof course over lintel absent or damaged.

Remedies	1 Remove excess mortar from cavity and repair defective areas. 2 If only one or two wall ties are not properly bedded they could be rebedded. 2) Where large areas are affected, weatherproof 3) the wall using a waterproofing treatment, rendering, or covering it with ship-lap board or tile hanging etc. 4 Insert or replace damp-proof course if possible otherwise weatherproof wall as 3.

Cross references	Part I page no	Part II other defect sheet references		Part III slide no
	14	B6	D8	48
	17	B7	D9	49
		D7		50

Defect	PATCHY DAMP NOT ASSOCIATED WITH RAIN
Location	Walls
Symptoms	Patchy damp areas appear initially on internal plasterwork, accompanied by peeling wallpaper, discolouration or, after a longer period, surface stains or mould growth.
Checks/ questions	* Is the damp independent of rain? * Are there any obvious leakages from pipes, cisterns or tanks? * Does the damp follow use of bath, basin or sink? * Is the rising main buried in the wall?
Action	Instruct repair of obvious leakages from pipes, cisterns or tanks. Otherwise refer to surveyor.

Defect	PATCHY DAMP NOT ASSOCIATED WITH RAIN	H5
Location	Walls	

Causes	1 Leaking or possibly backfalling overflow pipes.
	2 Leaking pipes embedded in the wall (often found in older properties) might remain undetected until frost damage or corrosion result in leakage.
	3 Localised chemical action.
	4 Leaking waste pipes.
	5 Localised condensation over buried rising main.

Remedies	1 Check for possible back-fall in overflow pipe. Check operation of ball valve, adjust, rewasher, renew as necessary.
	2 Replace embedded pipes and redecorate.
	3 Remove plaster in defective area and replace with new covering fixed on battens, redecorate.
	4 Repair or replace waste pipes, dry out area and redecorate.
	5 Replace rising main, or cover, insulate and redecorate area over buried pipe.

Cross references	Part I page no	Part II other defect sheet references	Part III slide no
	17 55	D7 F2 D8 F5 D9	

Defect	GENERAL DAMP NOT ASSOCIATED WITH RAIN
Location	Walls
Symptoms	General damp or patches of damp occur particularly in kitchens and cold bathrooms. Moisture beads appear on the surface of dense materials (eg concrete lintels above windows) and there may be signs of rusted metal fittings and in extreme cases, mould growth.
Checks/ questions	* Is the damp independent of rain? * How long has the damp been apparent? * What is the room used for? * What kind of heaters are used? * Have any changes been made to the type and amount of heating in room? * What ventilation is there? * Does the ventilation work or is it blocked?
Action	Refer to surveyor.

Defect	GENERAL DAMP NOT ASSOCIATED WITH RAIN	H6

Location	Walls

Causes	1 The most likely cause is condensation of water vapour in the air coming into contact with cold surfaces such as concrete lintels or other cold bridges at window frames and junctions of walls and floors. In cold, poorly insulated rear extensions condensation is likely to occur with intermittent use of heating or inadequate ventilation, particularly with paraffin heaters, where water is one of the products of combustion. 2 Condensation within the thickness of the wall itself. 3 Residual water.

Remedies	1 Improve ventilation, provide a more adequate or better distribution of heat such as background heating, or provide a higher standard of insulation on areas subject to condensation. 2 Consider providing a vapour barrier over affected areas. 3 Dry out residual water or introduce ventilation to allow it to dry out naturally.

Cross references	Part I page no	Part II other defect sheet references	Part III slide no
	17 54 45 55	D7 D8 D9	51 52

Defect	DAMP CHIMNEY BREAST
Location	Chimney breasts
Symptoms	Damp is visible on the surface of a chimney breast or flue. The patch remains damp irrespective of rain and decoration can be discoloured. The fault is often apparent in older houses (60-100 years old).
Checks/ questions	* Is the damp worse in wet, misty or muggy weather? * What type of appliance does the chimney serve? * Is the flue fitted with a liner? * Is there any obvious cracking or distortion of the chimney stack?
Action	Refer to surveyor.

Defect	DAMP CHIMNEY BREAST	H7
Location	Chimney breasts	

Causes	1 If the damp depends on rain, it is probably due to absent or defective damp-proof course or flashings in the chimney stacks.
	2 The chimney pot and/or its bedding on the stack may be defective, allowing penetration of water.
	3 Chemical action (open fires).
	4 Condensation in unlined flue (solid fuel, gas or oil-fired boiler).
Remedies	1 Examine damp-proof course, flashing and chimney stack for defects and carry out repairs.
	2 Replace or rebed pot.
	3 For badly affected areas, techniques involving covering, relining or replastering are possible.
	4 Reduce condensation by lining the flue with impervious liner or flexible metal pipe, depending on type of appliance.

Cross references	Part I page no	Part II other defect sheet references	Part III slide no
	15 17	D7 D8 D9	53

Defect	DAMP WALL OR CEILING
Location	Internally below parapets
Symptoms	Damp is visible on the internal plaster of the upper parts of external walls of a building. Initially damp appears at the wall/ceiling junction and it may then spread downwards. It will be particularly pronounced after heavy rain or snow.
Checks/ questions	* Is the damp more pronounced after heavy rain or snow? * Are there any obvious signs of a damp-proof course in the parapet? * Are there any obvious splits at the junction of parapet and roof? * Is the gutter behind the parapet cracked or leaking? * What is the condition of the flashings? * Is the gutter or the outlet blocked?
Action	Refer to surveyor.

Defect	DAMP WALL OR CEILING	H8
Location	Internally below parapets	

Causes	1 The absence or ineffectiveness of damp-proof course in the parapet.
	2 Splits at the junction of the roof finish and parapet or any flashing.
	3 Condensation.
	4 Cracked, leaking or blocked guttering on outlet behind parapet.
	5 Gutter full of frozen snow which blocks the downpipe flow then thaws in gutter and overflows.

Remedies	1 Take down and rebuild the parapet in order to add or replace a damp-proof course. If the damp-proof course exists already, check that water running off it does not run into the wall.
	2 Repair defective parapet/roof junction.
	3 Provide additional insulation.
	4 Repair or clear gutter or outlet.
	5 Fit bigger flashings and improve overlap into the gutter.

Cross references	Part I page no	Part II other defect sheet references		Part III slide no
	17	B1	D7	54
	54	B2	D9	55
	55	B6	D11	

Defect	DAMP CEILING UNDER FLAT ROOF
Location	Underside of flat roofs
Symptoms	Damp patches are visible after rain and in more severe cases water may drip from them for some time afterwards. They may also occur in periods of dry cold weather but they are more likely to be associated with the areas around the perimeter of the roof. Such patches may be brownish in colour and water may drip from cracks in the ceiling or from electric light fittings.
Checks/ questions	* Is damp associated with rain or does it follow periods of cold weather ? * Are there any obvious defects to the roof surface ?
Action	Refer to surveyor.

Defect	DAMP CEILING UNDER FLAT ROOF	H9
Location	Underside of flat roofs	

Causes	
	1 Condensation of water vapour passing from the room below the ceiling into the structural part of the roof. This is very likely in dry cold spells.
	2 Residual construction water entrapped during roof laying. This can cause trouble for years.
	3 Direct rain penetration, although possible, is much rarer than might be thought. Where water does enter, it may travel horizontally between layers of roof felt before appearing as damp.

Remedies	
	1 Provide an efficient vapour barrier on the surface of the ceiling and ventilate any air spaces in flat roofs. Perhaps improve insulation.
	2 Drain off trapped moisture by drilling temporary drainage holes and insert ventilation units.
	3 Repair defects in roof surface and at the edges, whether contributing to the damp or not.

Cross references	Part I page no	Part II other defect sheet references		Part III slide no
	17 18	B1 B2 D7	D9 D11	56

Defect	DAMP CEILING UNDER PITCHED ROOF
Location	On ceilings under pitched roofs
Symptoms	A wet patch is seen on the ceiling, perhaps either during or shortly after rain or snow.
Checks/ questions	* Is the damp obvious only after rain or snow? * Are there any obvious holes in the roof? * Are there any obviously defective tiles or slates? * Does the wet patch correspond to holes, defective tiles or slates? * Are there any obvious defects to valley or parapet gutters? * Is a water tank above the damp patch?
Action	Instruct repair to obvious holes and inform surveyor.

Defect	DAMP CEILING UNDER PITCHED ROOF	H10
Location	On ceilings under pitched roofs	
Causes	1 Defective tiles or slates. 2 Defective battens to which tiles and slates are attached (woodworm or fungal attack). 3 Defective parapet or valley gutters. 4 Leaking water tank.	
Remedies	1 See appropriate defect for remedial 2 action. 3 Patch perforated guttering, provided holes are small and not too frequent. Otherwise replace the gutter. 4 Repair or replace water tank.	

Cross references	Part I page no	Part II other defect sheet references			Part III slide no
	17	B4	D7	F1	57
	18	B5	D9	F2	
		B6	D11	H12	

Defect	PERSISTENT DAMP
Location	Solid ground floors
Symptoms	The floor surface is persistently damp except in very dry weather. Tile flooring materials laid on top become quite damp; carpet or lino laid on an apparently dry floor is covered with a mould growth on the underside or, in extreme cases, has rotted.
Checks/ questions	* Is there any record of a damp-proof membrane having been used in the construction? * What is the extent of the damp? Is it generally present or confined to the perimeter of the floor only?
Action	Refer to surveyor.

Defect	PERSISTENT DAMP	H11
Location	Solid ground floors	

Causes	1 Absent or ineffective damp-proof membrane. Damp rises from the ground, passing through the base concrete and floor material laid on top of it. Carpeting or lino may retain damp which would otherwise evaporate.
	2 Where the damp is restricted to the perimeter it may be due to the fact that the floor damp-proof membrane and wall damp-proof course have not been adequately linked.

Remedies	1 Remove base concrete; insert damp-proof membrane and relay concrete base. Allow it to dry out adequately before laying flooring materials.
	2 Cut perimeter of floor and insert impervious material of vertical damp-proof course.

Cross references	Part I page no	Part II other defect sheet references		Part III slide no
	17 28	D9 E5 E6	E8 E9	58

Defect	DAMP NOT ASSOCIATED WITH RAIN OR CONDENSATION
Location	Ceilings and floors
Symptoms	Damp patches are present on ceilings or floors, not near external walls.
Checks/ questions	* Where is the damp patch relative to the position of toilets? * If spasmodic, has the damp patch any thing to do with the emptying of appliances or movement of water? * Are there any obvious breakages of appliances, leaking joints or pipe work?
Action	Instruct repair and inform surveyor.

Defect	DAMP NOT ASSOCIATED WITH RAIN OR CONDENSATION	H12
Location	Ceilings and floors	
Causes	1 Leaks from broken appliances. 2 Leaks from defective joints and pipes. Note that damp resulting from defective appliances, joints and pipes may well show itself some way from the source since small leaks will run down and along pipes and ductwork before dropping onto other surfaces.	
Remedies	1⎞ Locate and repair all broken appliances, leaking 2⎠ joints or defective pipework. Allow damp areas to dry out. Redecorate as necessary.	

Cross references	Part I page no	Part II other defect sheet references			Part III slide no
	55	D9 D11 E5	E6 E8 E9	F1 F2 H10	59

DEFECTS IN APPEARANCE

The figures in the boxes on the opposite page are the reference numbers of the defect sheets which explain how to deal with the defects.

Questions to ask which will lead you to the correct defect sheet:

WHAT IS THE DEFECT ?

IS IT ON AN EXTERNAL SURFACE OF THE BUILDING ?

IF AN EXTERNAL DEFECT, IS IT ASSOCIATED WITH A WALL OR THE ROOF ?

IS IT CONFINED TO AN INTERNAL SURFACE ?

IS IT ASSOCIATED WITH A WALL OR A CEILING ?

J

WHAT IS THE DEFECT ?	WHERE IS THE DEFECT ?			**J**
	External wall	Roof	Internal wall	Ceiling
Dirty patches			J1	J1
Patchy white deposits	J2		J2	
Growth	J3	J3	J4	J4
Discolouration over radiators			J1	J1

DEFECTS IN APPEARANCE

Defect	DIRTY PATCHES
Location	Internal surfaces
Symptoms	Surfaces sometimes show distinct areas which are dirtier than others (pattern staining); the pattern may depend on what is behind the surface. Upstairs ceiling surfaces may be dirtier where there is no joist immediately above than where there is a joist.
Checks/ questions	* What is the structure above or behind the stained surface ? * Does the pattern of dirtiness correspond to the shape of structure behind the surface ? * In the case of upstairs pattern-stained ceilings, has insulation been laid between joists in the roof space ? * Are the dirty patches near warm spots such as radiators, hot pipes or light bulbs ?
Action	Refer to surveyor.

Defect	DIRTY PATCHES	J1
Location	Internal surfaces	

Causes	1 Dust and dirt tend to collect on the relatively colder parts of surfaces. On ceilings where there is no insulation between joists, the parts immediately under a joist are marginally warmer and therefore cleaner.
	2 Air currents caused by heat (radiators, light bulbs) allow more dust to be deposited than on surfaces where the air is still.

Remedies	1 Insulate roof space and redecorate as necessary.
	2 If possible, reduce or deflect hot air currents; redecorate.

Cross references	Part I page no	Part II other defect sheet references	Part III slide no
	26 27 28	D7	60

Defect	PATCHY WHITE DEPOSITS
Location	External and internal surfaces
Symptoms	<u>Efflorescence</u> may appear as a white fluffy powdery substance or a hard glassy deposit on external or internal surfaces. It is often seen on brickwork during the first dry period after building but may occur regularly after prolonged rain. Internally, it may be found under paint and wall paper or on plaster which has not been decorated. <u>Lime bloom</u> is a white stain on external surfaces near to concrete, eg brickwork at the ends of concrete sills.
Checks/ questions	* Are the patches present inside or outside ? * Are they localised or general ? * Is the house of brick construction ? * Are the patches near concrete ? * How long ago was the building completed ? * Has the defect occurred during the first dry period after building ? * Does it occur regularly after periods of prolonged rain ? * Is the stain soluble in water ? (Yes = efflorescence, No = lime bloom.)
Action	Refer to surveyor.

Defect	PATCHY WHITE DEPOSITS	J2
Location	External and internal surfaces	

Causes	1 Chemicals in the bricks are dissolved by water and come to the surface where they form as crystals when the surface dries. On external walls this is obvious but internally the efflorescence may be under the decorations. This may lead to crumbling of plaster and/or loss of adhesion of decorations.
	2 Lime bloom is formed by the leaching out of lime from cement and its chemical conversion to chalk. It is not soluble in water.

Remedies	1 Brush powdery substance off the surface. If it returns, it is because the surface has not fully dried out or, because the source of damp is still present. The damp must therefore be cured.
	2 Lime bloom can only be removed by washing with diluted acid. Strict safety precautions are necessary.

Cross references	Part I page no	Part II other defect sheet references	Part III slide no
	14	A9	61
	26	D7	62

Defect	ALGAE, LICHEN AND MOSSES
Location	External surfaces
Symptoms	Various coloured growths may be seen on the external surfaces of buildings, particularly in moist conditions.
Checks/ questions	* Is the growth localised or more general? * Is it a green, red or brown powder which may be slimy when wet? (Algae.) * Is it like leathery plates of tissue with tiny orange or green cups? (Lichens.) * Is it green and mossy? * Are gutters choked with loose moss?
Action	Refer to surveyor.

Defect	ALGAE, LICHEN AND MOSSES	J3
Location	External surfaces	
Causes	Growths thrive in damp conditions with chemicals found in roof coverings (tiles, slates etc). Growth is usually fairly gradual and may not be unsightly.	
Remedies	If necessary, remove growth with toxic wash followed by wire brushing, and remedy dampness. Ensure gutters do not become blocked.	

Cross references	Part I page no	Part II other defect sheet references	Part III slide no
	14	B7	63 64

Defect	MOULD GROWTH
Location	Internal decoration and paintwork
Symptoms	Grey, green, black or brown spots or patches are seen on internal decorations which may have spread to form a furry layer. Paintwork may show signs of pink or purple discolouration. Affected areas are likely to be damp.
Checks/ questions	* Is there any evidence of damp with the discolourations ?
Action	Refer to surveyor.

Defect	MOULD GROWTH		J4
Location	Internal decoration and paintwork		
Causes	The main cause is damp. The airborn spores of various mould growths thrive on damp surfaces. Surfaces subject to condensation or any persistent damp are particularly susceptible.		
Remedies	Remedy dampness, strip off decorations, treat surface with fungicide (poisonous material), redecorate. If not possible to eliminate the damp completely, materials for decoration should be resistant to mould growth.		

Cross references	Part I page no	Part II other defect sheet references	Part III slide no
	27 55	H1 to H12	65

MATERIALS

The figures in the boxes on the opposite page are the reference numbers of the defect sheets which explain how to deal with the defects.

Questions to ask which will lead you to the correct defect sheet:

WHAT IS THE DEFECT OR EVIDENCE FOR
DEFECTIVE MATERIAL?

WHAT IS THE MATERIAL AND LOCATION?

K

WHAT IS THE DEFECT?	WHERE IS THE DEFECT?		K
	Timber	Metal surfaces	Joint between components of walls and frames
Musty smell, discolouration, mushroom fungus (dry rot)	K1		
Smell, discolouration, spiders web type fungus (wet rot)	K2		
Small holes and dust (insect attack)	K3		
Lack of strength (dry rot, wet rot or insect attack)	K1 K3 K2		
Discolouration, rusting, pitting, perforation		K4	
Sagging or shrunk sealants			K5

MATERIALS

Defect	DRY ROT
Location	Timber
Symptoms	A musty or mouldy smell may be detected and a reddish brown dust and flat mushroom-like growths may appear. Timber with dry rot lacks strength, crumbles easily and is dull brown in colour. Deep cracks divide the wood into brick-shaped areas.
Checks/ questions	* Is the timber wet or very damp? * Is there any obvious reason for damp? * Is there a musty or mouldy smell? * Are there any signs of reddish dust? * Is there any sign of a silky white sheet or pearly grey felt-like growth? * Is there any evidence of flat mushroom-like growths, particularly at timber joints?
Action	Refer to surveyor.

Defect	DRY ROT	K1
Location	Timber	

| Causes | Normally timber has a slight moisture content but very damp timber is prone to dry rot. The growth originates from reddish brown airborne spores which attach themselves to the damp wood and then spread as a silky white sheet or greyish felt-like growth. This feeds on the wood which becomes dry and loses its strength. The flat mushroom shaped growths seen at joints are the fruit' of the fungus and these produce further spores.

Lack of ventilation is often the cause of humid conditions and moistness. |
|---|---|

| Remedies | Eliminate damp and dry out surrounding area. Provide adequate ventilation, particularly in the case of suspended floors.

Remove all timber showing signs of rot, cutting well back beyond the area of attack and burn immediately. Treat adjacent areas of timber to eliminate all traces of fungus.

Timber for repairs should be treated with preservative. |
|---|---|

Cross references	Part I page no	Part II other defect sheet references	Part III slide no
	10 54	B3 C1 E1	66

Defect	WET ROT
Location	Timber
Symptoms	Wet rot usually affects timber which has remained wet for a long time, such as areas in contact with wet walling. The timber is weak and dark in colour. Any cracking is less deep than that seen in a dry rot attack and there are rarely signs of fungal growth or spores. If visible, the fungus is usually slender, threadlike and dark coloured.
Checks/ questions	* Are there obvious reasons why the wood is wet? * Is there any sign of fungal growth?
Action	Refer to surveyor.

Defect	WET ROT		K2
Location	Timber		
Causes	Wet rot is caused by various fungi feeding and growing on wet timber and weakening it.		
Remedies	Eliminate cause of wetness and thoroughly dry out. Cut out the decayed timber and burn it, replacing with sound wood treated with preservative.		

Cross references	Part I page no	Part II other defect sheet references	Part III slide no
	10	B3 C1 E1	67 68

Defect	WOODWORM
Location	Timber
Symptoms	The surface of timber is disfigured with small circular or oval holes. The outer layers of wood may be weak and, in extreme cases, destroyed. There may also be dust near the holes.
Checks/ questions	* Ensure that holes are not man-made (eg where lino has previously been tacked down). * Is the attack localised or are there signs of attack in other areas?
Action	Refer to surveyor.

Defect	WOODWORM
Location	Timber
Causes	The cause is insect attack. Insect eggs laid in the surface of timber hatch into larvae which bore their way into the wood, feeding on it as they go. After a lengthy period (not less than one year) the fully developed beetle then eats its way out of the wood. Both softwoods and hardwoods are attacked, depending on the species of insect.
Remedies	Remove affected wood and replace or strengthen depending on the extent and severity of attack. Treat the whole area with insecticide. Ensure that adequate ventilation is provided. There are many specialist firms who are capable of applying appropriate treatments and identifying the characteristic holes and dust patterns produced by different insects.

Cross references	Part I page no	Part II other defect sheet references	Part III slide no
	10	B3 E1	69

	CORROSION
	Metals
Symptoms	The symptoms of metal corrosion include: * Expansion of metal thickness (eg rusting of steel) * Perforation of metal * Surface pitting (eg some aluminium alloys) * Discolouration (eg rust stains, green stains on copper).
Checks/ questions	* Which symptom is evident? * What metal is it? * Are there signs of damp? * Are two different metals in contact?
Action	Refer to surveyor.

Defect	CORROSION	K4
Location	Metals	

Causes	1 Atmospheric corrosion due to damp and possible pollution.
	2 Chemical corrosion.
	3 Water trapped between folds, laps and joints.
	4 Bi-metallic corrosion between two dissimilar metals.
	5 Corrosion due to stress which causes metal cracks.

Remedies	Patch or replace corroded metal parts, applying a protective coating (eg paint) where appropriate. If possible, eliminate cause of damp conditions.

Cross references	Part I page no	Part II other defect sheet references		Part III slide no
	12	B6 C4 F1	F2 F5	70

Defect	SHRUNK OR SAGGING SEALANTS
Location	Joints between components
Symptoms	The sealant in a filled joint may have shrunk or sagged resulting in water penetration.
Checks/ questions	* Where is the joint ? * Are there any signs of water penetration ?
Action	Refer to surveyor.

Defect	SHRUNK OR SAGGING SEALANTS	K5
Location	Joints between components	
Causes	Sealants in vertical joints particularly have to withstand different degrees of movement, intended or otherwise. The sealant used must match the extent of movement expected. Use of a sealant with too little resistance can lead to sagging.	
Remedies	If the joint is watertight, although the sealant is sagging, it is better left well alone. When remedial action is required, remove old sealant, clean out joint, and fill with sealant having greater resistance to sagging.	

Cross references	Part I page no	Part II other defect sheet references	Part III slide no
	13	A5 C2	71

Bibliography

The following are recommended for those who wish to study in more detail the defects covered in this book.

Common defects in buildings, H J Eldridge, Her Majesty's Stationery Office, 1976.

Basic guide to home plumbing, Readers Digest Association, 1976.

Basic guide to home electrics, Readers Digest Association, 1977.

Home electrics, G Burdett, Newnes Technical Books, 1977.

Condensation in dwellings - Part I, Ministry of Public Buildings and Works, Her Majesty's Stationery Office, 1970.

Condensation in dwellings - Part II, Department of the Environment, Her Majesty s Stationery Office, 1971.

Dampness in buildings, R T Gratwick, Crosby Lockwood Staples, 1974.

A dictionary of building, J S Scott, Penguin Books, 1974.

Index

A

Algae   J3
Appearance defects   D7, J
Asphalt   B1

B

Ball valves   F5
Basements – damp   H1
Bitumen felt   B2, H9
Blisters
  Asphalt   B1
  Decorations   D7, H2
  External paintwork to rendering   A9
  Felt roof   B2
  Sheet flooring   E9
Boilers   F10, F11
Brickwork
  Cracked   A1, B3
  Crumbling   A4
  Movement or bulging   A5

C

Cables   G1
Cavity walls   H2, H4
Ceilings   D
Ceilings – damp   B1, F1, H8, H9, H10, H12
Central heating   F11, F12
Chimneys   A
Chimney breasts – damp   A, H7
Chimney stacks   A, H7
Circuit breakers   G1
Cold water supply   F1, F2, F3, F5, F6
Cold water tanks   F1
Composition floors   E5
Concrete floor slabs   E4
Concrete screeds   E3
Corrosion – metal   C4, F1, F2, F5, F8, H5, H6, K4

Index

Cracking
  Asphalt   B1
  Chimneys   A2
  External walls   A1
  Floors   E3, E4
  Glass   C4
  Rendering   A7, A8
  Walls and ceilings   B3, D1, D2, D3

D

Damp   D7, D9, D11, E1, E6, E9, H
Damp-proof course   A5, E4, H2, H7, H8
Damp-proof membrane   E5, E8, E9, H11
Decorations – discoloured   C1, D7, H2, H5, J1, J4
Doors
  Binding   D10, E4
  Distorted   C6, D10
  External   C
  Faulty operation   D10
  Internal   C6, D10, E4
Drains   F
Drains – blocked   F9
Dry rot   K1

E

Efflorescence   A9, J2
Electrical appliances   G2
Electrical circuit overload   G1
Electricity – supply and distribution   G

F

Flat roofs   B1, B2, H6, H9
Floorboards – warped   E2
Floors   E
Floors – damp   H1, H11, H12
Floor screeds   E3, E7
Floor tiles   E3, E7, E8
Flues   D7, H7
Fuses   G1, G2

Index

G

Growths – mould, lichens etc   D7, H3, H5, H6, H11,
   J3, J4, K1
Gutters   A3, B6, H8, H10, J3

H

Hollow tiles   D8, E7
Hot water supply   F2, F4, F6, F10

I

Insect attack – timber   E1, K3
Internal finishes   D
Internal walls – cracked   D1, D2, D3

J

Joinery – external   C
Joinery – internal   D9
Jointing compounds   K5

K

Knocking – pipes   F6

L

Leaks
   Pipes   F2, H5, H10, H12
   Tanks   F1, H5
Lichens   J3
Lime bloom   J2

M

Magnesite floors   E5
Materials – defects   K
Mortar joints   A3
Mosses   J3
Mould growth   D7, H3, H5, H6, H11, J4

Index

O

Overflow   F5

P

Paintwork
  External   A9, C1, C2
  Internal   D11
Parapets   B1, B2, H8
Peeling paint   D11
Pipes
  Frozen   F3
  Furred up   F4
  Leaking   B7, F2, H5
Pitched roofs   B3, B4, B5, H10
Plasterwork   D1, D2, D3, D4, D5, D6, J2
Plastic wastes and traps   F7
Plastics laminates   D9
Plumbing   F
Plywood panels   C5
Putty   C1, C2, C4
Pvc tiles   E8

R

Radiators   F11
Rendering   A6, A7, A8, A9
Roofs   A1, B
Roof slates   B5, H10
Roof tiles   B4, H10

S

Sealants   K5
Sheet flooring   E9
Solid ground floors   E4, H11
Staining   J1
Surface finishes - joinery   D9

Index

T

Thermoplastic tiles   E8
Timber decay   C1, E1, K1, K2
Timber floors   E1, E2
Traps   F7

W

Walls
  Damp   A2, H1, H2, H3, H4, H5, H6
  External   A, H4
  Internal   D
Wall ties   D8
Warm air heating   F12
Wastes   F
Wastes - distorted   F7
Waste pipes - blocked   F3, F8
Water hammer   F6
Water heaters   F10
Wet rot   K2
Windows   C
  Cracked glass   C4
  Distorted   C3
Wood block flooring   E6
Woodworm   E1, K3